Carol Otis Hurst's

Picturing

ath

**Prekindergarten through
Second Grade**

sing Picture Books in the Math Curriculum

Carol Otis Hurst
Rebecca Otis

SRA/McGraw-Hill
Columbus, Ohio

Printed in the United States of America.

Send all inquiries to:

SRA/McGraw-Hill
250 Old Wilson Bridge Road
Suite 310
Worthington, OH 43085

ISBN 0-02-687367-2

2 3 4 5 6 7 8 9 NID 99 98

TABLE OF CONTENTS

TABLE OF CONTENTS

TABLE OF CONTENTS

INTRODUCTION

We all know the magic that can happen when we gather a circle of students around us and share a favorite picture book. We have known for a long time now that there are advantages to a shared good book over basal readers. The experience is more authentic for the students than the programmed text and allows students of various ability levels to focus less on their current level and more on the story itself and the power of language.

First and foremost, a good story can stand on its own. We must share with our children the experience of savoring a good story from start to finish—no "lessons," no pressures, no distractions. Share the power of the written word, the delight of good artwork, the humor of an author, or the illustrator's offbeat view of a common experience.

However, in addition to a rich supply of these unfettered experiences, we have discovered that sometimes the reading of a picture book is the perfect time to play with language, to notice how it works, and to reflect on what we know and what we are learning. In the context of story, there are many opportunities for leading the students to new discoveries. Similarly, there are opportunities to play with mathematical ideas and to make new discoveries about the mathematical world around us while sharing a picture book. Stories create their own world of possibilities and invite us to enter and explore.

Illustrations are rich with patterns, something the students are discovering as the basis of mathematics. Some books use those patterns in powerful ways that speak to us and to our students. The language of picture books is often patterned and rhythmic, again using a mathematical idea to create something powerful or playful. Picture books can open new areas of interest, inviting us to find out more, a perfect opportunity to collect data and look for the patterns that will help us understand. Furthermore, some picture books set before us problems that mathematical strategies can help us to solve: What do we know? What patterns can we see? How can these patterns help us predict possible solutions? How can we test these solutions?

Naturally, any good book can be used for explorations in most or all areas of the curriculum. Books are also a great vehicle for integrating all areas of your curriculum. In this book, however, we focus on mathematical ideas for using picture books. Ways of integrating mathematical concepts with stories and with the world around us are not always obvious, especially to those of us who were taught mathematics as anything but integrated. Here you will find many useful ideas and inspiration for your own ideas on integrating mathematics with the rest of your curriculum.

How This Book Is Organized

Generally, there is a great deal of overlap among the math concepts that children in these developmental stages are being exposed to. Sequencing, ordering, numeration, and one-to-one correspondence often blend together. All of these are interwoven with time and money. Likewise, patterns, attributes, and classification are often used together. Although each of these can be distinctly defined, their use in mathematics is not so neatly segmented. In spite of these limitations, we have chosen to classify the activities according to the one or two main categories upon which they focus.

Many of these categories have different names, depending on the preferences of organizations and math programs. We have chosen the following category labels to help you find what you're looking for in the activities. We define what we mean by each category and what is included under that category in the Concept Categories section of this book.

Attributes & Classification
Patterns
Problem Solving
Numeration
Geometry & Spatial Sense
Measurement
Time
Money
Data Gathering & Analyzing
Computation
Estimation
Perspective
Fractions & Proportion
Probability

Section 1: Individual Books

Any picture book can be used to approach math concepts: you can always count or classify characters or items. Those activities, however, superimpose math on the book or stretch a book to fit into math. Other picture books are written expressly to explore a math concept: counting books and books about shapes, money, or time, for instance. The books we've listed in this section are neither of the above. These are books that are good stories—interesting books in and of themselves. Looked at with a mathematics lens, however, they can be something more. They can provide an opportunity to talk and think mathematically without destroying the story.

In this section, we have suggested 50 books. We'll give you the bibliographic information, tell you what the book is about, and then list some things you and your students can do to make the mathematics connection.

Section 2: Picture Books and Math Concepts Chart

We have taken all the titles mentioned in this book and charted them so that you can find, in one place, areas in which the various books can be used. For instance, if you know that a particular student or group of students is ready for activities about money, you can scan this chart for books that are checked under the Money column to see which of these you might have in your classroom or your library. (Page numbers are listed for easy reference.) At the same time you can, if you choose, see which of these are also marked under geometry and spatial sense because your class has also been playing with these concepts lately.

Section 3: Math Concept Categories

In this section, there are twelve chapters, each centered on a different mathematical concept. Within these chapters, we tell you what we mean by these categories, and we list the related concepts included under that heading.

You'll find a number of suggested activities for working with each concept here. These are activities that are appropriate with many different picture books, exploring such things as illustrations, plots, and characters. There are ways to find and play with patterns, activities for measurement, and investigations for collecting and analyzing data, among others.

Following the activities, we've listed picture books that are particularly well suited for use with the concept. Again, books that we developed in an earlier section are listed under the concepts in which they are strongest along with other titles that work well with this concept. You'll also find recommended books that are written especially for mathematics.

Section 4: Annotated Bibliography

The booklist contains an alphabetical listing of the books we have called attention to throughout the book.

Appendices

Appendix A: Counting Books
The number of good counting picture books is astounding. Here is an annotated listing of recommended titles.

Appendix B: Professional Resources
We listed a few good professional resources for integrating the math curriculum.

Index
In the back of this guide is a comprehensive index that will assist you in finding specific ideas and books.

Section 1

Individual Books

WHO SANK THE BOAT?

written and illustrated by Pamela Allen
Putnam, 1990
ISBN 0-698-20679-7

Quién hundió el bote?
SRA, 1995. Available in Big Book and Small Book formats.

SUMMARY

A cow, a pig, a sheep, and a mouse decide to take a boat ride. Guess who gets in last. Guess who sinks the boat. They enter the boat from biggest to smallest, and each new passenger tips the boat and causes it to sit lower and lower in the water.

Grades 1-2
Measurement

How much does each of these animals really weigh? List them from largest to smallest.

Grade 2
Estimation & Computation

Estimate the weight of each animal and the accumulated weight as each new passenger boards the boat.

K-Grade 2
Data Gathering & Analyzing

Make small wooden shapes to represent the boat and designate rocks or other objects to represent each of the passengers. Float them in water. Can you work it so that the last and smallest object sinks the boat? Does it make any difference in which order you put the animals in the boat? Try it and see whether you're right. How could you change the ending of the story?

Grade 2
Measurement

Make different boats of many materials. Which ones float best? Measure the boats—their weight, dimensions, volume, and volume of water displaced—to see why they float or sink.

K-Grade 2
Attributes & Classification

Assemble a group of materials that you think might float. Try them. Make lists of materials under two headings: Floating and Non-Floating.

Grades 1-2
Patterns

Find the pattern in the text. Put the pattern sentences "Was it the _____ who _____ ? No, it wasn't the _____." on a pocket chart. Give children picture cards or word cards to place in the blanks to make new pattern sentences.

Amelia's Road

written by Linda Jacobs Altman
illustrated by Enrique O. Sanchez
Lee & Low, 1993
ISBN 1-880000-04-0

Summary

Amelia hates roads and maps because her family travels to pick crops and, whenever her father takes out the map, she knows they will soon move on. This time she particularly hates to leave because she has found a teacher who has bothered to learn her name. Amelia finds a deserted road that she calls her own and buries some of her treasures beside it. Now she has a place and she doesn't cry this time when her father takes out the road map.

K–Grade 2

Attributes & Classification

Amelia drew a picture of her dream, which was a house. Draw pictures of your dreams and then find ways to sort those dream pictures.

Grades 1–2

Geometry & Spatial Sense

On a large sheet of drawing paper, put a shape to represent your home near one side of the paper. On the other side, put your school. Put other shapes to represent buildings or places you pass on the way to school. Use a crayon to draw on the paper as you tell people about the way you get to school.

Grades 1–2

Classification & Attributes

Amelia buries a box of things that are important to her. Put small things into a container to represent what is important to you. Bring it to school and share it with others. Tell them what each object represents and why it is important.

K–Grade 1

Numeration & Estimation

Throughout the book there are pictures of the fruits and vegetables Amelia and her family pick. Sometimes the fruits and vegetables are lined up on the page and are easy to count. Other times they are in baskets or on the ground. Count or estimate the number of fruits and vegetables on each page.

K–Grade 2

Data Gathering & Analyzing

On the first page of the story, the author tells us that Amelia hated all kinds of roads: straight, curvy, dirt, and paved. Are there other kinds of roads? List them and then decide what kind of road each member of the class lives on. On a small square of paper, draw the kind of road you live on. Place the square on a chart beside other roads that are the same as yours. On what kind of road do most people in your room live? On what kind of road do the fewest live?

Guess Who My Favorite Person Is

written by Byrd Baylor

illustrated by Robert Andrew Parker

Simon and Schuster, 1992

ISBN 0-684-19514-3

Summary

The narrator joins a girl in her game called "tell-what-your-favorite-thing-is." But this isn't the usual "my favorite color is blue." You have to tell what kind of blue. The game continues with the blue of a lizard's belly and the sound of hundreds of bees buzzing. What's your favorite place to live, favorite thing to see moving, favorite dream? The descriptions are evocative and the illustrations are a dreamy match for the tone of the story.

PreK–Grade 2

Data Gathering & Analyzing

Discuss how you would answer some of the questions. Conduct a survey of answers and see whether there are any patterns by which you can categorize the answers.

PreK–Grade 2

Attributes & Classification

Form discussion groups to play the girl's game. What's your favorite kind of blue? What's your favorite thing to touch? What are some things you really like that most people don't like or don't notice? Describe what you like about them.

PreK–Grade 2

Patterns

Look for patterns in the book. There are natural patterns in some of the illustrations, but did you notice the pattern of the placement of text on the page? Then, of course, there's the pattern of the game itself.

Daley B.

written by Jon Blake
illustrated by Axel Scheffter
Candlewick, 1992
ISBN 1-56402-078-9

Summary

Daley B. is an animal with a problem: he doesn't know what he is. He doesn't know where to live or what to eat, and he doesn't know why his feet are so big. He surveys many possibilities and decides to live in a tree and eat acorns, but he still doesn't know what his large feet are for. When a weasel tells Daley, "I eat rabbits! Rabbits like you!" Daley B. is stunned to find out that he is a rabbit, but he doesn't have to think first to use his large feet to boot away the weasel. All the other rabbits rush out to tell Daley B. he's a hero. "That's funny, I thought I was a rabbit."

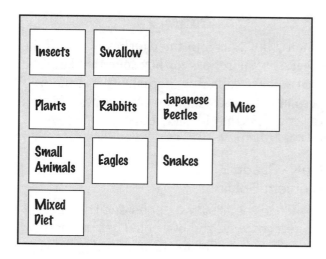

PreK–Grade 2
Data Gathering & Analyzing

Gather diet information about a large selection of animals. Categorize the types of food they eat and make an index card for each category. Post the cards in a column down the left-hand side of a bulletin board. Make an index card with the name of each animal you researched. Put the animal's index card next to the category of food it eats, letting the line of index cards next to the categories create a horizontal bar graph. Which food is eaten by the most animals? Is it eaten by a lot more animals or by a few more animals than the next food?

PreK–Grade 2
Data Gathering & Analyzing

You can make a similar chart about where animals live.

PreK–Grade 2
Attributes & Classification

What other ways can you classify the animals you researched?

Grades 1–2
Problem Solving

What was Daley B.'s problem? What methods did he use to solve his problem? What other methods could he have used to find solutions to this problem?

Beware of Boys

written and illustrated by Tony Blundell
Morrow, 1992
ISBN 0-688-10925-X

Summary

When a boy falls into the clutches of a wolf, he suggests some recipes for boy soup that keep the wolf so busy gathering ingredients that the wolf becomes exhausted and the boy escapes. This is a clever turn to the old folktale about stone soup.

PreK–Grade 2
Problem Solving

Read the first two pages and then brainstorm ways the boy could get out of the jam he's in. Follow through by figuring out the possible consequences of some or all of the suggestions.

K–Grade 2
Attributes & Classification

In each recipe, there are some items no one could eat. Make a list of those things.

K–Grade 2
Patterns

Predict what the boy will do with the items you listed in the above activity. Check the last illustration to see whether you're right.

K–Grade 2
Attributes & Classification

On index or blank playing cards, draw and label pictures of all the items in the two recipes. Place the cards face down on the table. Each person draws two cards and names something the two items have in common. The next player adds a card and names something the three items have in common. Continue until no commonality can be found.

Grade 2
Estimation & Measurement

Some of the items in the recipes have an exact measurement; others do not. Using the illustrations and your own common sense, give more exact measurements for such things as an *oodle, well-full, foothill, moo-cow,* and *birdbath.*

Grades 1–2
Measurement & Fractions

Make up your own recipes for boy, girl, teacher, or parent soup. You might want to use all nonstandard measurements.

K–Grade 2
Measurement, Fractions, & Proportion

Find a real recipe for stew or pie and make it.

Grades 1–2
Estimation & Time

How long would it take the boy to build the wall at the mouth of the cave? After you estimate, use a timer while you pantomime getting the ingredients, mixing cement, and laying just a few bricks.

THE MITTEN: A UKRAINIAN FOLKTALE

written and illustrated by Jan Brett
Putnam, 1990
ISBN 0-399-21920-X

El mitón

SRA, 1995. Available in Big Book and Small Book formats.
Available on audiocassette from Scholastic.

SUMMARY

After a young boy loses a white mitten in the snow, many animals decide it's perfect for their shelter. Bigger and bigger animals enter the mitten, each using its unique weapon. It's a mouse that undoes the whole thing by making a bear sneeze.

PreK–K
Spatial Sense

Put a big mitten and some small toy animals on the table. Move the animals around and describe the positions of the animals in relation to the mitten.

Grades 1–2
Measurement & Estimation

Find out how long and how wide each of the story animals is in real life and estimate how big the mitten would have to be to hold them all.

K–Grade 2
Attributes & Classification

Sort mittens from the lost and found box in as many ways as possible.

Grades 1–2
One-to-One Correspondence & Attributes

Make two sets of cards: one with names or pictures of the animals who took shelter in the mitten and the other with the attributes of those animals. Mix and match the cards, first realistically and then fantastically.

K–Grade 2
Sequencing

The frames in this book contain a sort of subplot. List the sequence of events in the frames and the major illustrations.

K–Grade 1
Sequencing

Outline the steps the grandmother takes to make the mittens.

Grade 2
Time

Figure out how much time passes between the events by comparing the action in the mitten and in the frames to what the boy is doing.

Town Mouse, Country Mouse

written and illustrated by Jan Brett
Putnam, 1994
ISBN 0-399-22622-2

Summary

Most of us are familiar with the story of two mice out of their element, trying to cope with unfamiliar worlds, but Brett provides a twist to the tale. Here a country mouse couple exchanges houses with a pair of city mice. The tale proceeds in the familiar pattern until the end when a city cat and an owl, each in pursuit of the mice, literally bump into each other and work out a similar exchange. Brett's illustrations are her usual intricate and detailed work and, also as usual, the action in the picture frames adds to the fun.

PreK–Grade 2
Problem Solving

There are several sets of problems in this book. List the problems and decide how they are solved and other ways they could have been solved.

PreK–Grade 2
Attributes & Classification

The mice call something a "cat with wings." List the ways in which the owl and the cat are alike. Make another list to show how they are different.

Grades 1–2
Attributes & Classification

Draw pictures of the animals from this book on index or blank playing cards. Make two cards for each animal. Play Concentration with the cards, allowing a match if the player can name at least three things that each of the turned-up animals have in common.

Grades 1–2
Attributes & Classification

Use the cards you made for Concentration to categorize the animals in as many ways as possible. Consider predator/prey status, size, physical appearance, and weapons of defense and attack.

Grades 1–2
Numeration

List and count the dangers for the mice in each world. List and count the pleasures of each world for them.

Grades 1–2
Data Gathering, Analyzing, & Computation

According to this book, which world is safer for mice?

PreK–Grade 2
Patterns

At the end of the book, the cat and the owl are about to change places. What dangers do you think the cat will discover in the woods? What dangers will the owl discover in the town? Will the cat and the owl return to their own homes?

Benny's Pennies

written by Pat Brisson
illustrated by Bob Barner
Doubleday, 1993
ISBN 0-385-41602-4

Summary

Benny has only five new pennies, and he's got lots of family telling him what they want him to buy. When he returns, he has satisfied them all. Furthermore, his purchases are sensible and could conceivably be bought with the money.

Grades 1-2
Computation & Money

Using lots of pennies, show how many ways Benny could have spent the money: two pennies for one gift, three pennies for another, and so on.

Grades 1-2
Computation & Money

Change the prices to two cents each, five cents each, and ten cents each. How much money would Benny need to complete these transactions?

Grades 1-2
Computation & Money

Do other word problems. What if Benny wanted to buy three roses and two fish? What would they cost?

K-Grade 1
Numeration & Money

Look at the pictures in which Benny is holding pennies in each hand. Make various combinations of five pennies.

K-Grade 1
Money

Make a chart to show how Benny spent his money.

THE PICNIC

written and illustrated by Ruth Brown
Dutton, 1993
ISBN 0-525-45012-2

SUMMARY

Rabbit and his friends bolt for cover when humans arrive in their field for a picnic. Confronted at the entrance to the rabbit hole by a curious toddler and then by a dog trying to dig in, they are saved by a sudden downpour that forces the family and their dog to leave. Seen from the animals' point of view, this realistically drawn wordless book effectively presents a familiar scene from a new perspective.

PreK–Grade 2
Perspective

How does the perspective of the wild animals differ from the perspective of the people and the dog? What new information do you get from the animals' viewpoint that the people aren't aware of?

PreK–Grade 2
Perspective

Read other books with unusual perspectives, such as *Do Not Disturb* by Nancy Tafuri, *The Giant's Toe* by Brock Cole, *Town Mouse, Country Mouse* by Jan Brett, and *Two Bad Ants* by Chris Van Allsburg. For older students, read chapter books like *Shoebag* by Mary James (Scholastic, 1992. ISBN 0-5990-43030-0), *The Shrinking of Treehorn* by Florence Perry Heide (Holiday House, 1971. ISBN 0-8234-0189-8), and *Fantastic Mr. Fox* by Roald Dahl (Random, 1986. ISBN 0-394-90497-4).

Grades 1–2
Data Gathering, Analyzing, & Perspective

With the previous or similar books, create a chart that lists the point of view for each book, the point of view from which we would typically see each story, and what we know from that unusual viewpoint that we would not know otherwise.

Grades 1–2
Data Gathering & Analyzing

Make a list of animals that interest you and find out what you can about how people affect those animals. Sort the data into categories, such as the degree of human influence, the beneficial and harmful effects of that influence, and ways to reverse or offset the harmful effects.

PreK–Grade 1
Geometry & Spatial Sense

Use a large box to create an animal burrow for free play in a drama corner.

Grade 2
Data Gathering & Analyzing

Conduct a survey of opinions about dogs. What do people like about dogs? What bothers them about dogs? How do they think dogs affect the environment? Do they have a dog? If you have access to a computer and the Internet, survey a class in a different environment. Compare the answers you get.

No Problem

written by Eileen Browne
illustrated by David Parkins
Candlewick, 1993
ISBN 1-56402-176-9

Summary

Mouse is given a "some assembly required" kit by Rat. From Rat's note, she understands that it is something to ride and so, without reading the instructions, she assembles a vehicle and rides it. However, it doesn't work well, and so other animals try their hands at it. Each creates a vehicle and gives it a name, but the kit doesn't go together correctly until Shrew finds and reads the directions, dissembles the vehicle, and categorizes the parts. Then the animals ride to Rat's house in an airplane.

PreK–Grade 2

Attributes & Classification

In each vehicle, name as many parts as you can. Make a list of the parts you see.

K–Grade 2

Attributes & Classification

Look at each vehicle the animals build. What do the vehicles have in common?

Grades 1–2

Attributes, Classification, Data Gathering, & Analysis

Bring in as many instructions for making or playing things as possible. Read one set of instructions aloud without telling the others what you are talking about. Can they figure it out? Classify the sets of instructions according to length, complication, and whether or not diagrams help.

Grade 2

Attributes & Classification

In this story, the shrew is the animal that solves the problem. Find information about real shrews. Is there a reason the author chose a shrew for this role? For what attributes are the other animals known?

PreK–Grade 2

Problem Solving

Each animal says there's "No problem." Is there? What is the problem? Try assembling the airplane shown on the book cover without reading the directions. Can you do it? What helped you?

The Mouse and the Apple

written and illustrated by Stephen Butler
Morrow, 1994
ISBN 0-688-12811-4

Summary

A mouse sits under an apple tree and waits for its lone ripe apple to fall. One by one, other animals join the mouse until there are five animals waiting for the apple to drop. As each animal grows impatient, it tries in vain to make the apple fall and then leaves in disgust, declaring it rotten, sour, hard, or soft. When all are gone except the patient mouse, the apple falls and it's delicious.

PreK–K
One-to-One Correspondence

Place a green tree on a flannel board. Let the children retell the story as they first put an apple on the tree and then place the animals under it in the order in which they arrive. Have other cloth apples for the children to place on the tree so that each animal can have one.

K–Grade 1
Numeration

Use the same flannel board setup as in the above activity. As the children tell the story, ask them how many animals are under the tree.

PreK–K
Geometry & Spatial Sense

Again using the flannel board story, as you or the children place the animals under the tree and apples on the tree, accent the prepositions *on* and *under*. Ask the children to place one of the apples or animals elsewhere on the flannel board and tell where it is in relation to the tree.

PreK–K
Geometry, Attributes, & Classification

Cut out and laminate circular shapes to represent apples, oranges, peaches, grapefruit, and mangos. Also cut out some noncircular fruits, such as watermelons and bananas. Let the children sort the fruit shapes, giving their reasons for classification. If they don't mention shape, you might want to point it out to them.

PreK–K
Patterns

Find the patterns in this story. Did you find the patterns in the tree and cow or the pattern in the story itself?

THE TINY SEED

written and illustrated by Eric Carle
Picture Book Studio, 1991
ISBN 0-88708-015-4

SUMMARY

It's fall and the seeds are being blown along by the wind. One is smaller than the rest, but one by one something happens to the others. They land on mountain tops, deserts, or oceans; are eaten by birds or mice; or are smothered by weeds, until the tiny seed grows into the only surviving plant. It flowers and scatters its seeds to the wind.

PreK–Grade 1

Attributes & Classification

Go on a collecting walk to gather wild seeds in the fall. See how many different kinds of seeds you can find. Categorize your seeds when you get back to the classroom.

PreK–Grade 1

Patterns

Chart the lifecycle of the seed in the book, noticing the cyclical pattern. What are some other cyclical patterns that exist in nature?

PreK–Grade 1

Geometry & Spatial Sense

Use the illustrations to point out spatial relationships. "The seeds are over the ocean." "The seeds are under the snow." "Where are the seeds now?"

Grade 1

Perspective

Notice the viewpoint of the seed. What is different about how the seed sees things?

THE GIANT'S TOE

written and illustrated by Brock Cole
Farrar, 1986
ISBN 0-374-32559-6

SUMMARY

This is a sort of prequel to the story of Jack and the beanstalk. A giant hacks off his toe and it becomes a small boy. The boy cooks the giant's hen that laid the golden eggs and throws away his harp. The giant is displeased, to say the least.

Grades 1–2

Measurement & Estimation

Estimate the size of the giant by looking at the pictures of Jack and then at the pictures of the giant. Compare the giant's size to things like trees, your house, and your school.

Grades 1–2

Measurement

On the playground, draw an outline of the giant as big as you think he is. Measure the giant with your own feet and with as many other units of measurement as possible. Record your data.

Grade 2

Measurement

Compare the size of your giant to the size of real animals. How does he compare to an elephant, a blue whale, or various dinosaurs? Use a bar graph to show your results.

Grade 2

Estimation

The giant says he's going to dig a hole to China. How deep would that hole have to be? Use a globe to figure out which country you would get to if you could dig a hole from where you are now all the way through the Earth.

The Magic School Bus Inside the Human Body

written by Joanna Cole
illustrated by Bruce Degen
Scholastic, 1989
ISBN 0-590-40759-7

El autobús mágico en el cuerpo humano
Spanish version available from Lectorum. Big Book format available from Scholastic.

Summary

This book in the popular Magic School Bus series finds Ms. Frizzle taking her class on a field trip to the science museum to study the human body. Once again, however, the unexpected happens and Ms. Frizzle ends up driving them into Arnold's body for a close-up view. The zany story is packed with information about the human body.

PreK–Grade 2
Measurement

Compare the sizes of parts of your body. Use manipulatives or adding machine tape at the lower grades and standard measurements at the higher grades.

K–Grade 2
Data Gathering, Analyzing, & Measurement

Take a survey of information about our bodies: height, weight, length of hair, shoe size, and basic fingerprint type.

K–Grade 2
Attributes & Classification

Make a chart showing the places the class visits in Arnold's body. List the attributes of each part, such as size, location, and function.

Grades 1–2
Measurement

Can you figure out what sizes the children shrank to by looking up the actual size of some of the body parts around them?

PreK–Grade 1
Spatial Sense

Notice the positions of the kids in the body. Describe what you see. "They are inside the body. They are going out of the blood stream."

Grades 1–2
Geometry & Spatial Sense

Notice the shape of the body parts and the organs. Does a body part's shape serve a purpose? What advantages might there be to the various shapes?

PreK–Grade 2
Patterns

Notice the wild patterns in Ms. Frizzle's dresses. Create more patterns based on a similar science theme.

Grades 1–2
Patterns

Examine your fingerprints. Can you identify the main types of swirls? Which type do you have? Do all of your fingers have the same type? How many others in your class have the same type of swirls?

Grade 2
Numeration

The book says there are 250 million red blood cells in a drop of blood. How much is 250 million? What can you compare it to? You can read *How Much Is a Million?* (see page 85) to get an idea.

Grade 2
Computation

If there are 250 million red blood cells in a drop of blood, how many are there in an average human body?

K–Grade 2
Data Gathering & Analyzing

Keep track of everything you eat for a day. Compare the foods to the nutritional food pyramid. Calculate the servings from each food group and see whether you are within the range of recommendations.

Grades 1–2
Data Gathering & Analyzing

Calculate the nutritional components of your school lunch and compare it to the recommended daily allowances of various nutrients.

MISS RUMPHIUS

written and illustrated by Barbara Cooney
Penguin USA, 1982
ISBN 0-670-47958-6

La señorita Emilia
Available from Lectorum.

SUMMARY

Through the eyes of her grand-niece, we learn of Miss Rumphius's childhood relationship with her grandfather and her fascination with his life. Miss Rumphius then tries to accomplish in her life the three things suggested by her grandfather: to travel widely, to live by the sea, and to leave the world more beautiful. She accomplishes the third by planting lupines everywhere she goes.

PreK–K
Attributes & Classification

Fill the water table with various kinds of seeds for free exploration. Use sieves to separate seeds of different sizes. Use seeds that are inexpensive and untreated, like bird seed. Use the seeds to feed the birds when you're finished.

K–Grade 2
Attributes & Classification

Examine a variety of flower seeds. Sort them by attributes such as size, color, and shape.

Attributes & Classification

Cut flower pictures from seed catalogs and classify the flowers in as many ways as possible.

Patterns

Follow the developmental sequence of a flowering plant. In addition, you can grow flowers in pots from bulbs, such as amaryllis and paperwhites.

Patterns

Describe patterns in the illustrations. Look for the obvious geometric patterns in windows and buildings as well as the more complex patterns in things like the lupine spikes and the evergreen trees.

Problem Solving

Discuss ways to leave the world more beautiful.

Patterns

What is the repeating pattern in Miss Rumphius's, her grandfather's, and the narrator's lives?

Estimation & Time

If the scene at the end of the book where Miss Rumphius is talking to the young Alice is the present, in what year did the story begin? At what time was she working in the library? Planting flowers? Find out about clothing, vehicles, and other signs of the times and confirm or modify your estimates.

So Many Cats!

written by Beatrice Schenk de Regniers
illustrated by Ellen Weiss
Houghton, 1985
ISBN 0-89919-700-0

Summary

They started with one lone and rather lonely cat, and then there were more. Some came on their own. Others were given to them. The cats came singly and in groups, and each had its own name and personality. As each cat becomes a part of the household, the author re-counts them and gets a new number. The repetitive text is charming, and the plot is one to which most cat owners can relate.

Attributes & Classification

Look at the cats on the cover. Describe one, without pointing to it, so that others can figure out which cat you mean.

Attributes & Classification

Draw and cut out twelve cat figures. Color them in the way in which the cats in the book are colored. Figure out ways to group the cats. Let others guess what your sorting rule is.

Grades 1-2
Computation

Make a list of the cats in the groups in which they came: 1 cat, 1 cat, 3 cats, 1 cat, 1 cat, 3 cats, 2 cats. Figure out how many there are all together. Notice that on the first page the author says they have a dozen cats. Now change as many numbers in the above list as you can and still end up with a dozen cats.

PreK-Grade 2
Problem Solving

Imagine that the people in your home allow you to have one cat: the first one in the book. Now imagine that you want to take in the second cat. What arguments would your household have against taking the cat? What arguments would you give for taking it? Do the same for each new cat in the book.

PreK-Grade 2
Data Gathering & Analyzing

In the book, you never see a picture of a whole person, only parts of people. How many people do you think live in the house? What evidence do you have?

PreK-K
Attributes

Create a household of cats on paper. Make sure that each cat is different in at least one way from every other cat.

Grade 2
Fractions & Proportion

On what page are half of the dozen cats in the house? Can you figure out when a quarter of them are there? How about three quarters? Is there a time when a third of them are there? Change the groupings from the story if you have to.

The Mouse Who Owned the Sun

written by Sally Derby
illustrated by Friso Henstra
Simon and Schuster, 1993
ISBN 0-02-766965-3

Summary

Mouse lives alone in the deep, dark woods. He's content with his existence, mostly because he believes he owns the sun. He thinks so because he gets up early every morning and asks the sun to rise and it does. At night, when he is sleepy, he gets into bed and asks the sun to set and it follows his orders. One day when exploring farther than he had ever been, Mouse is discovered by the King's soldiers. The soldiers believe Mouse is the owner of the sun when he commands it to be dimmed and a cloud happens to cover it. The King too is convinced and offers to buy the sun from Mouse. Mouse trades ownership of the sun to the King in exchange for a map, the first he's ever seen.

Data Gathering & Analyzing

Make a list of the things that happen to make Mouse think he owns the sun. Make another list of things that could happen that would let Mouse know he is wrong.

Geometry & Spatial Sense

Make a map of Mouse's travels. Describe his route using spatial words such as around, in back of, across, in front of, and beside.

Patterns

What pattern convinced Mouse that he owned the sun? What pattern can you discover that will allow you to predict (or command) certain things, such as the ringing of a dismissal bell, the contents of your lunch today, what someone in your house will say when he or she comes home, and so on?

Patterns

What was the pattern of Mouse's day before this story? What changes do you think there will be? What might have been the King's daily routine before the story? Will there be changes? Will those changes make him think he owns or doesn't own the sun?

Attributes & Spatial Sense

Gather together as many different kinds of maps as possible. Use globes as well as picture, topographical, and political maps of many sizes. Explore the maps and make comparisons among them.

YERTLE THE TURTLE AND OTHER STORIES

written and illustrated by Dr. Seuss
Random, 1956
ISBN 0-394-80087-7

Available on audiocassette from David McKay.

SUMMARY

Dr. Seuss attacks mindless authority and vanity through the fable of Yertle the turtle king who orders all the turtles in the pond to form a throne that is high enough for him to see for miles around. It's the lowly turtle Max, at the bottom of the pile, who topples the throne of a king. Other stories in the book are "Gertrude McFuzz" and "The Big Brag."

Measurement

Make a life-size cutout of one turtle. Trace around it on the playground or sidewalk until you have Yertle's throne. Measure your turtle throne with other objects. How many children high is the throne? How many schoolbooks high is it?

PreK-Grade 1
Measurement, Numeration, & Patterns

Use blocks to make Yertle's throne. How many blocks can you put in the throne before it topples? Does it matter how many blocks wide the throne is? Does it matter how you stack the blocks? Is there a pattern that works best?

Grades 1-2
Estimation, Geometry, & Spatial Sense

The higher Yertle's throne, the farther he could see. How far do you think you could see from the highest spot at your school? From the highest building in your town?

Grades 1-2
Measurement & Classification

Find the place in the story "Gertrude McFuzz" where you think she could still fly.

Look in a bird book for birds with big tails. Make a list of them. Are any big-tailed birds good flyers?

Grades 1-2
Numeration and Computation

Dr. Seuss said that Gertrude didn't stop eating berries until she'd eaten three dozen. How many berries is that? Are there other things in your classroom that number more than a dozen? More than two dozen? More than three dozen?

PreK-Grade 2
Numeration

Create pictures of birds with fancy tails. Count the number of tail feathers on the bird with the fanciest tail.

Eppie M. Says . . .

written and illustrated by Olivier Dunrea
Simon and Schuster, 1990
ISBN 0-02-733205-5

Ana B. dice . . .
SRA, 1995. Available in Big Book and Small Book formats from SRA.

Summary

Ben Salem tells us all about his big sister, Eppie M., whom he thinks knows everything. Eppie M. has filled Ben Salem with many "facts," such as walking backwards will get you to Australia and kissing a mama pig on the nose will turn you into a prince. Ben faithfully tries out each of Eppie M.'s truisms. Sometimes he proves her wrong, sometimes right, and sometimes he concludes that he doesn't have enough information yet. The country setting and language, as well as the precise and comic illustrations, make this book a charmer.

K-Grade 2
Logic

Make a list of everything Eppie M. says. Which do you think could be true? What makes you think so?

K-Grade 2
Data Gathering & Analyzing

On a chart, make a list of each thing Eppie M. says. Next to each item, write what happened when Ben tried it. Try some of them yourself or imagine that you did and put your discoveries in the last column. Did any of Eppie M.'s statements turn out to be true?

K–Grade 2
Logic

Look at the list of things Eppie M. says again. Can you change some words and make them more likely to be true?

K–Grade 2
Data Gathering & Analyzing

Make a chart with three columns. In one column put what Eppie M. says. Label that column "What Eppie M. Says." In another column make up your own statements. They can be as outlandish as Eppie's, more likely, or a little of both. Label that column "But I Say." In the third column, write the statements that are more likely to happen.

SHOES FROM GRANDPA

written by Mem Fox
illustrated by Patricia Mullins
Orchard, 1990
ISBN 0-531-08448-5

SUMMARY

In this cumulative tale, each of Jessie's relatives buys her an article of clothing to go with the shoes from Grandpa. Illustrated with cut-paper collage, the book is light and playful as Jessie's costume becomes more elaborate. In the end, she begs for a pair of jeans and takes off on her skateboard.

K–Grade 1
Numeration

When the pattern first becomes clear, ask the children "Who else will give her clothing? How many items of clothing will she end up with?"

Grades 1–2
Money & Computation

This book can lead you to discussions of clothing and wardrobe. How much does an outfit cost (new or second-hand)? How much do you save with hand-me-downs?

PreK–K
Numeration

How many different colors of paper are used in one illustration?

PreK–Grade 2
Patterns

Find patterns in the illustrations of the clothing and find patterns in your own clothing. How can you describe these patterns? How can you represent them?

K–Grade 2
Attributes & Classification

When the artist creates something like a pair of pants, she uses many shades of the same color to create texture and shadow. Notice places where this is particularly well done. How many different shades does she use? Use multiple shades of tissue paper to make your own original creations.

PreK–Grade 2
Geometry & Spatial Sense

Look again at the illustrations. Which pieces of paper are on top of others?

Which are underneath? How many layers of paper can you find piled up?

K–Grade 1
Problem Solving

What is Jessie's problem? How could she have solved it? What solution does she choose? How do others react to her choice?

SECRET FORESTS

A COLLECTION OF HIDDEN CREEPY CRAWLY BUGS AND INSECTS

written and illustrated by Michael Gaffney
Artists and Writers, 1994
ISBN 0-307-17505-7

SUMMARY

This over-sized informational book shows the creatures of one habitat in isolation on a page with a brief text about that creature. The following page shows the creature camouflaged in its habitat. The book provides many opportunities for browsing and casual learning, as well as for finding specific information.

PreK–Grade 2
Patterns

This whole book has a pattern. Can you decide what it is?

PreK–Grade 1
Geometry

Look at the bugs as they appear on the white pages. How many are triangular? Can you find any that are almost square or round? Look at their shadows.

Sometimes their shadows help them make more shapes. Make a list of the shapes you find in and around the bugs.

PreK–Grade 2
Patterns

Look at the patterns on the wings of some of the insects. Use paint, crayon, or cut paper to make your own insect wings.

Grades 1–2
Patterns

Use cardboard or sponges to make insect stamps. Print your stamps in patterns across a page. See whether other people can discover your pattern rule and predict which insect you would print next. Add a new color or insect and make new patterns.

Attributes & Classification

Copy the pictures of the individual insects and put them on attribute cards. Sort the cards. Ask others to decide what your sorting rule is. Take turns sorting the cards and guessing the rules.

Attributes & Classification

Use the insect attribute cards to play Concentration. Deal all the cards face down on a table. Take turns turning over two of the cards. If you can name something the two insects have in common (besides being insects, that is), take the two cards away.

ONCE UPON MACDONALD'S FARM

written and illustrated by Stephen Gammell
Simon and Schuster, 1984
ISBN 0-02-737210-3

Erasé una vez, en la granja del señor MacDonald
SRA, 1995. Available in Big Book and Small Book formats.

SUMMARY

MacDonald's farm had no animals, so he bought an elephant, a baboon, and a lion. When the animals get fed up with MacDonald trying to milk them and get them to lay eggs, they leave. His neighbor comes to the rescue and gives MacDonald a horse, a cow, and a chicken. All seems well until MacDonald starts his chores for the day using the chicken to pull the plow.

Patterns & Problem Solving

Once the story gets going, stop at various points and ask for predictions for what might happen next. Why? How many possibilities can you think of?

Data Gathering, Analyzing, & One-to-One Correspondence

Find out about farm animals and how they're used on farms. Select one use for each animal and then mix and match the uses to come up with other silly things MacDonald might do with farm animals.

Data Gathering & Analyzing

After gathering information about the uses of farm animals, categorize the animals according to their uses. What other animals could MacDonald have gotten eggs from, milked, or used for plowing?

Attributes & Classification

Find other books in which people do silly things. What do the books have in common? How are they different?

PreK–Grade 2

Attributes & Classification

Look at the illustrations in *Once Upon MacDonald's Farm*. What do you notice about them? In what ways are they different from other illustrations you have seen? Go through some of your books, comparing illustration techniques and styles. Create categories and tabulate your findings. Younger children might group the books in piles, and other students can tally the numbers. Report the findings.

Cactus Hotel

written by Brenda Guiberson
illustrated by Megan Lloyd
Henry Holt, 1991
ISBN 0-8050-1333-4

Summary

This book follows the life of a saguaro cactus from the time it is a tiny seed until its death at two hundred. We also learn a lot about the desert and the animals that depend on the saguaro for food, water, and shelter.

K–Grade 2

Patterns & Sequencing

Examine other books centered on the life cycle of a plant, such as *The Tiny Seed* by Eric Carle.

K–Grade 2

Measurement

Use adding machine tape or long strips of paper to make replicas of the cactus at its various heights. Find something in your school that is the same height.

Grades 1–2

Patterns, Data Gathering, & Analyzing

Investigate the life cycle of a plant that is important in your area. In addition to general information, compare quantitative facts, such as height and length of life span, to the saguaro cactus.

K–Grade 1

Attributes & Classification

Make a chart of the animals that visit the cactus and list why they visit. Categorize them according to the reason for their visits and graph the results.

Grades 1–2

Data Gathering & Analyzing

Make a chart of desert creatures. List how they cope with desert conditions, such as water shortage and heat. Show your findings on a picture graph or bar graph.

Hungry Hyena

written by Mwenye Hadithi
illustrated by Adrienne Kennaway
Little, 1994
ISBN 0-316-33715-3

Summary

Hungry Hyena has tricked Fish Eagle out of his meal of fish for the last time. Fish Eagle and Pangolin plan a trick of their own, which has Hungry Hyena and all the other hyenas climbing atop each other to try for "the sweetest meat in all the world." When their tower topples, they all limp away. From that day on they are slower runners and, perhaps, wiser by having been taught a lesson about their greediness.

Grades 1–2
Attributes & Classification

From this book you can jump off into folktales and folktale-style books. Look for some of the common types of folktales, such as *pourquois* stories, stories of tricksters, and stories of fools.

PreK–Grade 2
Patterns

The watercolor illustrations are a lush environment abounding in patterns. Categorize the different types of patterns you find and use manipulatives to represent some of the patterns. Use some of your favorite patterns to create your own paintings of Africa.

PreK–K
Attributes & Classification

Choose an animal in one of the illustrations and make a list of its attributes.

Grades 1–2
Estimation, Computation, & Measurement

How far is the moon? How tall is a hyena? How many hyenas would it take to reach the moon? Estimate and then find the facts, revising estimates as you gather the facts. Do the final computations to verify your estimates.

Grades 1–2
Problem Solving

What was Fish Eagle's problem? What other solutions might Fish Eagle have used? Did the outcome in the story solve the original problem?

Chickens Aren't the Only Ones

written and illustrated by Ruth Heller
Putnam, 1981
ISBN 0-448-01872-1

Las gallinas no son las únicas
Available from Lectorum.

Summary

This strikingly illustrated nonfiction book is about egg layers. In rhythmic text and vibrant paintings, we see domestic birds and wild birds, insects and dinosaurs. Every egg layer Heller could find is here.

Grades 1–2
Attributes & Classification

What categories does Heller use to organize this book? What other categories could she have used?

K–Grade 2
Sequencing & Patterns

Studying and comparing life cycles provides many opportunities for sequencing and detecting patterns. Draw the life cycle of a couple of insects. Now start with another insect and guess what might come next in each stage based on the patterns of other insects' life cycles.

Grades 1–2
Data Gathering & Analyzing

Conduct a survey asking people what kinds of animals lay eggs. How many of the major groups of animals did each person list? What type of animal was most often overlooked?

Grades 1–2
Data Gathering, Analyzing, Classification, & Attributes

Chart the different types of animals listed in the book. What are their similarities? What are their differences? Do they have anything in common besides laying eggs?

Grade 2
Patterns, Data Gathering, & Analyzing

Continue the pattern of the book by creating a sequel about live-born offspring.

PreK–Grade 2
Patterns

Notice and discuss the different patterns and types of patterns in the paintings of animals in the book. Older students can choose a favorite pattern in the book and design a wallpaper, wrapping paper, fabric print, multimedia background, or other repeating design based on their favorite pattern in the book. Some computer drawing and painting programs make it easy to test different patterns and color combinations and to create perfect repetitions of them.

Chester's Way

written and illustrated by Kevin Henkes
Morrow, 1988
ISBN 0-688-07608-4

Chester, un tipo con personalidad
SRA, 1995. Available in Lap Book and Small Book formats.

Summary

Chester and Wilson are the best of friends and do everything exactly alike. They dress in matching costumes for Halloween and photocopy their holiday wish list because they always want the same things. Then Lilly moves into the neighborhood. She dresses in disguises and always carries a water pistol, just in case. This is the story of how they resist her presence and then eventually learn to appreciate her differences as well as the ways in which she is like them.

PreK–Grade 2
Data Gathering & Analyzing

Begin a listing of things Chester and Wilson have in common. For each item, see whether there is a corresponding way in which Lilly is different.

PreK–Grade 2
Patterns

What will happen now that Victor has moved into the neighborhood?

K–Grade 1
Numeration, Attributes & Classification

How many different disguises does Lilly use in the book? The answer depends on which outfits you consider disguises. You can list the disguises in two groups: definite disguises, which everyone agrees on, and possible disguises, about which there is not agreement.

PreK–Grade 2
Data Gathering & Analyzing

Take a survey about some of the things mentioned in *Chester's Way*. For each question, place containers with two different colors of manipulatives, one color for each possible answer to the question. Each student in turn takes a manipulative representing the color of their answer to the question and puts it in a third container for answers. When everyone has answered, the container is emptied and its chips counted. If the manipulatives are stackable, a separate stack for each color gives a graphic representation of how people answered. Do more people do it one way? Do a lot more people do it that way or just a few more?

There can, of course, be more than two responses to a question. You can translate the responses to conventional graphs. You can also add preferences not mentioned in the book. Students can also question people outside the classroom and compare the statistical results with their class's results.

Julius, the Baby of the World

written and illustrated by Kevin Henkes

Morrow, 1990

ISBN 0-688-09700-6

Julius, el rey de la casa

Available from Lectorum.

Summary

Everyone loves the new baby—except Lilly, his big sister. She sabotages her parents efforts at good parenting by telling Julius he's ugly and by teaching him the alphabet all mixed up. She does everything she can to make his life miserable until her cousin starts saying the same mean things about Julius. Then Lilly's hackles are raised to defend him, and she discovers, to her surprise, that he is soft and sweet and lovable. The book is funny and compassionate even though it deals with strong feelings and a standard plot.

K–Grade 2

Attributes & Classification

The intensity of Lilly's feelings provides an opportunity to notice and describe different kinds of feelings. Go through the book a second time, noting Lilly's feelings. Solicit as many descriptive words and phrases as possible. When you have finished, summarize the feelings Lilly experiences and the order in which she goes through them. Are there other situations in which you have experienced this sequence of feelings?

PreK–K

Attributes & Classification

Provide a wide selection of baby toys for free exploration. After all of the children have had sufficient time to explore freely, take the opportunity to discuss casually with them some of the physical attributes of the toys.

PreK–K

Geometry & Spatial Sense

Find Lilly on each page. Then encourage the use of position words and attributes as children describe Lilly's whereabouts. Sometimes she is obvious and sometimes less so.

K–Grade 1

Numeration

How many times does Lilly appear on each page? Encourage the children to explain how they arrived at their answers.

K–Grade 1

Numeration & One-to-One Correspondence

Choose a page and find out whether there are more Juliuses or more Lillys. Who appears more often in the book?

K–Grade 1

Patterns

Notice the patterns the author/illustrator uses to position the multiple-frame pictures on the pages.

Grades 1–2

Estimation

Given the number of pages in the book, estimate how many illustration frames there are in the total book. Discuss various ways of thinking about the problem and approaching the estimation.

Evan's Corner

written by Elizabeth Starr Hill

illustrated by Sandra Speidel

Penguin USA, 1991

ISBN 0-670-82830-0

Summary

Evan has a problem. He wants a place of his own, but there are eight people living in his two-room apartment. When his mother gives him a corner to call his own, he decorates it, filling it with a plant and a pet turtle to make it his. When he discovers something is still missing, his mother helps him see that helping his younger brother decorate a corner for his own brings Evan the happiness that has been just out of reach.

Grades 1-2
Problem Solving

What is Evan's problem at the beginning of the story? How does the problem change during the story? Chart the problems Evan experiences in one column, and in a second column list his solutions. What do the problems have in common? What do the solutions have in common?

Grades 1-2
Problem Solving

Brainstorm solutions to Evan's original problem. What are Evan's limitations in choosing solutions? Which possible solutions does this seem to eliminate?

Grades 1-2
Geometry

Evan's mother decides that with eight people living in the two rooms each person gets a corner. What other ways might the space be divided?

Grades 1-2
Computation

How many different arrangements are possible for eight people and eight corners? How can you find out? How about four people in four corners?

Grade 2
Geometry & Spatial Sense

How might your classroom space be divided among all the people who share it? What if instead of a space for each person, you divided into groups of 3 or 4 kids and each group had its own space? How would you divide the room?

PreK-Grade 1
Geometry & Spatial Sense

Divide into groups and give each group a section of the classroom for their own. Discuss spatial relationships as the children decide how to decorate their area.

Grades 1-2
Money & Fractions

The turtles are on sale for 50¢. Set 5 dimes on a table. Evan receives a dime each time he carries someone's groceries. How many dimes does he need to get 50¢? Move one dime to a new spot as he gets each dime for carrying groceries. At the end of the first day of carrying groceries, how far is he in earning his 50¢? Halfway? More than halfway?

My Place in Space

written by Robin and Sally Hirst

illustrated by Roland Harvey and Joe Levine

Orchard Books, 1990

ISBN 0-531-08459-0

Summary

Henry and Rosie tell the city bus driver that they want him to take them home. When he teases them that maybe they don't know the address of where they live, Henry rises to the occasion and tells the driver precisely where he lives: 12 Main Street, Gumbridge, Australia, Southern Hemisphere, Earth, solar system, solar neighborhood, Orion Arm, Milky Way Galaxy, local group of galaxies, Virgo Supercluster, the universe. During Henry's description, we also get a brief description of each part of the address. The result is a clear picture of our "place in space" as well as a glimpse at the amazing distances involved.

Grades 1–2

Measurement and Time

Chart the time it takes light to travel the various distances mentioned in the book.

K–Grade 2

Data Gathering, Analyzing, & Measurement

Graph distances to the places in the book using the speed of light as your unit. How will you approach the problem of the vast differences in the figures?

Grades 1–2

Numeration & Measurement

List the number and the unit of measure for each place described in the book. Take time to reflect on the numbers, what they mean, and how they are written.

K–Grade 2

Data Gathering & Analyzing

Graph the sizes of places mentioned in the book.

Grades 1–2

Geometry & Spatial Sense

What would you include as your address on Earth, assuming your address in the universe is the same as Henry's? What could you add besides the street, town, and country?

Grades 1–2

Spatial Sense

Create complex addresses for the locations of other things, such as a tree, an animal, a building, or your room at school.

Grade 2

Measurement & Computation

Traveling at 60 miles an hour, how long would it take to get from where you are to the center of Australia? To the center of the Southern Hemisphere? To the center of the Earth? To the center of the solar system? To the center of the galaxy?

Grade 2

Measurement & Computation

If you were to build a scale model of your place in space, what size would you make the Earth? Using this figure, calculate the size of the solar system, galaxies, and so on, according to the same scale.

Grades 1–2
Attributes & Classification

Obtain facts and pictures of many galaxies. Categorize the galaxies according to attributes. One resource with pictures of galaxies is Seymour Simon's *Galaxies* (Morrow, 1988. ISBN 0-688-08004-9).

Grades 1–2
Attributes & Classification

Classify a selection of stars by their attributes and find out what the classifications tell astronomers about a star.

Grades 1–2
Measurement & Computation

Discuss light years and other units of measure and then create some of your own. How fast does sound travel? How fast does a person run? How fast does a car travel? A bird? A cheetah? Convert some familiar distances to these units of measurement.

Grades 1–2
Numeration

This book goes well with *How Much Is a Million?* because of the central role of very large numbers. (See page 85.)

A House Is a House for Me

written by Mary Ann Hoberman
illustrated by Betty Fraser
Penguin USA, 1978
ISBN 0-670-38016-4

Available on audiocassette from Live Oak.

Summary

"A hill is a house for an ant, an ant./A hive is a house for a bee./A hole is a house for a mole or a mouse/And a house is a house for me!" Thus begins this illustrated poem of houses. It starts somewhat logically and gets sillier and sillier: "And pens can be houses for ink." The busy illustrations draw us into the pages where we find even more houses for things.

PreK–Grade 2
Attributes, Classification, & Spatial Sense

This activity is unavoidable. After reading the book, you will be looking for things in houses everywhere.

Grades 1–2
Attributes & Classification

Make up similar poems about some other quality, such as cereal is a breakfast for me or a coat is a coat for me.

PreK–Grade 2
Attributes & Classification

Search the illustrations for houses not mentioned in the text.

PreK–Grade 2
Patterns

Look through some of the illustrations for patterns. Describe the patterns you find. How are they different?

K-Grade 2
Patterns

Make your own "crowded" illustration. Include as many patterns as you can.

K-Grade 1
Numeration

Count the number of homes in one of the illustrations.

PreK-Grade 1
Attributes & Classification

Search the busy illustrations for other attributes: find something yellow, something soft, something alive, something slimy.

Alfie Gets in First

written and illustrated by Shirley Hughes
Morrow, 1982
ISBN 0-688-00849-6

Summary

Alfie, a boy of two or three, gets into the row house and slams the door, leaving his mother and baby sister outside while Alfie and the key are inside. Neighbors gather, as do the firefighters, but Alfie solves the problem himself.

PreK-Grade 2
Problem Solving

Figure out ways to solve this problem. Make a list and then decide which ways make the most sense.

PreK-K
Numeration

The helpers arrive in groups. Place counters in a line to represent the helpers as they get to the house.

Grade 2
Data Gathering & Analyzing

Graph the way Alfie feels with each event of the story, from the arrival home to the rescue. You could use picture graphs, bar graphs, or line graphs, showing the degree of happiness or confidence or the degree of unhappiness.

PreK-Grade 1
Attributes & Classification

Gather as many different keys as possible. Classify the keys in as many ways as possible.

PreK-Grade 1
Attributes & Classification

Go on a door walk. Notice the different kinds of doors on houses and buildings.

Grade 2
Data Gathering, Analyzing, Classification, & Attributes

On an outdoor walk, take notes about the different kinds of doors that you see. Try several ways to show the information you gathered.

The Doorbell Rang

written and illustrated by Pat Hutchins
Morrow, 1986
ISBN 0-688-05252-5

Llaman a la puerta
Available from Lectorum.

Summary

Ma has made a dozen cookies that Victoria and Sam are dividing between themselves, but the doorbell rings. Then there are two friends to share them with. Each time the kids get the cookies divided up the doorbell rings, until finally, it's grandma with more cookies.

PreK–Grade 2
Patterns

Find and describe some of the patterns in the illustrations. How can you represent these patterns with manipulatives?

K–Grade 1
Patterns

Use a pocket chart or write out a segment of the story on large strips, one strip for each line starting with "'That's six each,' said Sam and Victoria" and continuing through the first "'You can share the cookies.'" These eight lines create a repeating pattern through the rest of the story. Read the story aloud, following the pattern strips. Put the new words in a phrase over the original words as you go.

Grades 1–2
Computation

Follow the math of the story as you go. How many kids arrived? How many kids are there? How many cookies will each kid get? How did you figure that out?

Grades 1–2
Estimation

Estimate how many cookies Grandma brought. How can you be accurate without counting all the cookies?

Grades 1–2
Computation

After Grandma brought more cookies, how many cookies will each kid get? How many different ways can you use to figure that out?

Grade 2
Computation & Patterns

Notice how many kids share the cookies each time. Write the numbers on the chalkboard. How do you think the author decided what number of kids would arrive each time? How did you figure it out?

YONDER

written by Tony Johnston
illustrated by Lloyd Bloom
Penguin USA, 1988
ISBN 0-8037-0278-7

SUMMARY

This lyrical and beautiful book tells of a farmer and his wife who build a home and farm, plant a plum tree, and start their family. We watch the seasons pass and the family and tree grow until one becomes many.

Grades 1-2
Time & Estimation

On long strips of paper, draw pictures showing the chronology of events in this book. Estimate how long it takes a plum tree to grow big enough to support a swing. On your strip of paper mark that time. Estimate the age at which the girl would be old enough to marry and mark that time on the picture strip. Estimate the age of the man at the beginning of the book and at his death and mark those times.

PreK-Grade 1
Time

Decide what season it is on each page of the book.

Grade 2
Time & Estimation

From the beginning of the book to the end, how many times do you think they had fresh plums from the plum tree? How did you get your answer?

PreK-K
Patterns, Geometry, & Spatial Sense

Look at the picture of the quilt and find as many squares in it as you can. Remember that if you put four squares together you can get another square. Look at the fields on the page facing the quilt and find more squares. Are there squares in other places in the story?

Grade 2
Patterns

Use the pattern from this book to tell your own family's story.

REFLECTIONS

written and illustrated by Ann Jonas
Morrow, 1987
ISBN 0-688-06141-9

SUMMARY

This is a day in the life of a child by the sea, exploring the ocean, pond, and woods—but there's a twist. When you get to the end of the book, you flip it upside down and continue from the back page to the front. The boats on the sea at dawn, turned upside down, become birds and a plane in the sunset sky. This time everything looks different.

Grades 1–2
Perspective

Notice the things you see differently by flipping the picture over or because of the different text. Look for things that are hardly noticeable from one perspective but which become prominent from the new perspective.

Grades 1–2
Perspective

Create your own two-way art.

Grades 1–2
Attributes & Classification

Use the pictures in which an object represents two different things to ask yourselves: What makes a boat a boat? What makes a bird a bird? Which attributes of each object does the artist use to change your perception?

PreK–Grade 2
Attributes, Classification, & Patterns

Look for patterns in the illustrations. List patterns in two categories: natural and artificial. Now look at the patterns again and this time categorize them by the type of pattern: ABAB or ABCABC or non-linear patterns, such as concentric or checkerboard.

Grades 1–2
Patterns

Look for examples of symmetry in the illustrations.

Grades 1–2
Perspective

Look for other examples in artwork where perspective shifts, such as Escher's work and the famous two faces and a vase.

Grades 1–2
Spatial Sense

Create a fictional map showing the route taken by the narrator of the story. You will need to determine which places the narrator revisits in the story in order to create a path that fits these in.

Jump, Frog, Jump!

written by Robert Kalan
illustrated by Byron Barton
Morrow, 1981
ISBN 0-688-09241-1

Salta, ranita, salta!
Spanish version available from Lectorum. Big Book format available from Scholastic.

Summary

In this cumulative picture book, a frog catches a fly and escapes from a fish, a snake, a turtle, and more. How? "Jump, frog, jump!" The predictable refrain invites participation, and what looks like a capture at the end returns to "Jump, frog, jump!" after all.

PreK–Grade 1
Patterns

Discuss the repeating pattern of the text and the accumulation of predators.

K–Grade 1
Patterns

Read several cumulative tales such as *Hattie and the Fox, Shoes from Grandpa,* and *Why Mosquitoes Buzz in People's Ears*. Sing songs such as "Hole in the Bottom of the Sea," "Green Grass Grew All Around," and "She'll Be Comin' Round the Mountain." How are these stories and songs the same? In what ways can you describe the patterns?

K–Grade 1
Data Gathering & Analyzing

Gather information about the animals in the story and other animals to create food chains and food webs. What patterns do you see, and how can you categorize the different diets of the animals?

PreK–Grade 1
Geometry & Spatial Sense

Use the pictures and text to notice and describe the spatial relationships between the various animals in the story.

FISH FRY TONIGHT

written by Jackie French Koller
illustrated by Catharine O'Neill
Random, 1992
ISBN 0-517-57815-8

SUMMARY

When Mouse catches a fish, the biggest one she has ever caught, she is ecstatic. She gleefully invites Squirrel and some of his friends to dinner, declaring that she has caught a fish as big as she. Squirrel repeats the invitation to Rabbit, declaring that Mouse has caught a fish as big as he. The message and the increasing size is repeated through the woods. When Mouse opens her door to let her dinner companions in, she is aghast at their number and size. However, Mouse is resourceful, to say the least, and a good hostess.

K–Grade 2
Measurement

Use craft paper of different colors to cut out fish as big as each animal thinks Mouse's fish is.

Grade 2
Measurement, Data Gathering, & Analyzing

Find out the average size of each of the animals in the book. Then find out what kind of fish grows to be that size. Make a chart or graph to show the information.

K–Grade 2
Measurement & Ordering

Arrange the fish in order of their size.

K–Grade 2
Attributes & Classification

Cut fish out of a variety of colors of cardboard. Make some with top fins, others without. Make some with long tails and others with short tails. When you have a large number of fish, place them, one at a time, in such a way that each fish has only one attribute in common with the fish before it.

K–Grade 2
Attributes & Classification

Use yarn to group fish that have an attribute in common. Let others figure out the attribute. They can do so by naming it or by placing another fish within the set that they think fits. Another variation would be for you to place others that fit as they watch.

Grades 1–2
Fractions & Proportion

Estimate how much pizza each of the animals would eat. Decide how many pizzas Mouse should order.

PreK–Grade 1
Problem Solving

What was Mouse's problem? How did she solve it?

Sitting in My Box

written by Dee Lillegard
illustrated by Jon Agee
Penguin USA, 1989
ISBN 0-525-44528-5

Available in Big Book format.

Summary

A boy is sitting in a big cardboard box when some-one knocks. It's a giraffe—followed by an elephant, a baboon, a lion, a hippopotamus, and, finally, a flea. The text is rhythmic with a strong pattern.

PreK–Grade 2
Patterns

Chant the story together. In one reading most children can do it. Act it out.

Grades 1–2
Patterns

Clap the rhythm. Print the text on a chart. Then use colors and codes to take the place of the words.

PreK–Grade 1
Spatial Sense

Make statements using position words, such as "In the first picture, the boy is *in* the box. The animals are *outside* the box."

PreK–K
Sequencing

Use a big box and building blocks to rep-resent the animals. Demonstrate as you talk about the sequence of events: "First, a boy sat in a box. Next, a giraffe got in."

K–Grade 1
Numeration

Use the same box and blocks but use ordinal numbers in the statements:

"First, a boy was sitting in the box. Second, a giraffe got in. Third, an ele-phant got in."

Grade 1
Numeration

Make number statements, such as "The boy is in the box. That's one in the box. The boy and the giraffe are in the box. That's two in the box."

When the animals leave, make state-ments like "There were six in the box and the hippo jumped out. Then there were five in the box."

K–Grade 1
Computation

Turn the plot into a song that fits the tune of "Move Over." It could go something like

There was one in the box
And the tall giraffe said,
"Move over, move over."
So the boy moved over
And the giraffe got in . . .

There were six in the box
And the little flea said,
"Move over, move over."
So they all moved over
And the giraffe jumped out . . .

Do it in reverse order, also.

When This Box Is Full

written by Patricia Lillie
illustrated by Donald Crews
Morrow, 1993
ISBN 0-688-12017-2

Summary

A child looks at an empty box and imagines all the things she will put in it through the coming year. The months of the year are added to the left-hand page of each spread and the things that go in the box are representative of seasons and holidays.

PreK–Grade 1
Spatial Sense

Find or draw pictures of things you want to put in a box.

PreK–Grade 2
Geometry & Spatial Sense

Play a game. One person places a block or another object in relation to a box. Others, who cannot see the box, ask questions like "Is it in the box? Is it beside the box?" The person who figures it out gets to be the next placer.

Grades 1–2
Sequencing and Time

Practice saying the names of the months in order, starting with January and stopping at the month in which a birthday comes.

PreK–Grade 2
Attributes & Classification

Assemble boxes and containers. Group the boxes and then explain the reasons for the categories.

K–Grade 2
Attributes & Classification

Brainstorm ways in which the objects in the story can be categorized.

K–Grade 2
Classification

Each object in the book represents a month. Brainstorm for other objects that could represent the seasons, events, or holidays of various months.

PreK–Grade 2
Attributes & Classification

Many of the objects placed in the box are identified with a descriptive adjective: *wild* daisy, *red* leaf, *purple* egg. Find other words that could be used to describe each object.

PreK–K
Attributes & Classification

Find the page in the book that talks about the month that is the same as the current month. Talk about things you could place in a box for that month.

K–Grade 1
Numeration

How many objects went into the box each month? Was it the same number each month? Count the number of objects in the box at the end of the book.

Frog and Toad Are Friends

written and illustrated by Arnold Lobel
HarperCollins, 1970
ISBN 0-06-023958-1

Sapo y sepo son amigos

Spanish version available from Lectorum. Audiocassette available from HarperCollins.

SUMMARY

This easy-to-read book has been around a long time. The small book contains five short stories about a frog and a toad who are good friends despite their very different personalities.

PreK–Grade 2
Attributes & Classification

In "A Lost Button," Toad and Frog hunt for the button that Toad lost from his vest. They and others find many buttons, but each is different from Toad's button in one or more attributes. Collect as many buttons as possible. Sort them in many ways. Any classification is acceptable if you can explain it.

PreK–Grade 2
Attributes & Classification

From the button collection, select a button that could be the first button found. Then compare your button to each of the others until you find another button just like yours.

K–Grade 2
Sequencing

Glue the buttons to a strip of paper according to the order in which they appear in the story. Then draw pictures for the events surrounding the discovery of each button.

K–Grade 1
Time

In the first story, "Spring," Frog tears the pages off the calendar so that Toad will know it's spring. Go through the pages of a calendar together and talk about the seasons and weather on the children's birthdays.

PreK–Grade 2
Time

Try constructing the classroom calendar as a strip divided into days and, when the month is over, put the strips high on the classroom wall, letting the children get the idea that this month didn't disappear after it was over; it became the past. Refer back to the events on those classroom calendars frequently.

Grades 1–2
Measurement & Time

In the last story, Frog gives Snail a letter to deliver to Toad. It takes four days to get there. Speculate on how long it would take the letter to get there if Frog gave it to a rabbit, an ant, and so on. Remember, Frog got back to Toad in time to wait for the letter.

Chicka Chicka Boom Boom

written by Bill Martin Jr and John Archambault
illustrated by Lois Ehlert
Simon & Schuster, 1989
ISBN 0-671-67949-X

Big Book, Small Book, and audiocassette formats available from SRA.

Summary

A, B, and C climb up a coconut tree. Soon the rest of the letters follow. "Chicka chicka boom boom! Will there be enough room?" Naturally, it's not until the last letter, Z, climbs up that the tree sways over, spilling them all in a heap.

K-Grade 1
Numeration

Count the letters as they come into the picture.

K-Grade 1
Attributes & Classification

Identify the attributes of various letters, such as straight lines and curves, and color.

PreK-Grade 1
Measurement

Using a balance scale and plastic letters (like refrigerator magnets), can you set up the scale so that it tips when the Z is added?

K-Grade 1
Numeration

Rewrite the story with numerals instead of letters. How many numerals will you have climb the tree before they fall?

K-Grade 1
Measurement

Create another adventure for the letters. What will happen next? This might involve more experiences with weight, such as climbing in until they sink a boat; or size, such as crawling into a bag until it bursts.

PreK-Grade 1
Spatial Sense

After reading through the story, look at it together a second time. What is happening? Where are the letters going? Where are they now? Encourage the use of words that describe the spatial relationships of the letters.

PreK-Grade 1
Patterns

This story lends itself well to a strongly rhythmic reading. Clapping the time and synchronizing it to the words can take some practice.

The Salamander Room

written by Anne Mazer
illustrated by Steve Johnson
Random, 1991
ISBN 0-394-92945-4

Summary

A boy wants to keep the salamander he has found in the woods. His mother keeps asking questions like "Where will he sleep? What will he eat?" Each time the boy responds with an answer that makes sense as far as the salamander's life is concerned but which will eventually entail turning his room into a forest.

PreK–Grade 2
Problem Solving

What is the problem here? Can it be solved without destroying the boy's room? At what point does the boy's solution become impossible or at least impractical? Make a list of the problems and the boy's solutions.

Grades 1–2
Patterns

Make a flowchart of the questions the mother asks and the solutions. Do you see a pattern in the flowchart?

K–Grade 2
Spatial Sense and Measurement

Take a small carton or box and pretend it's the boy's bedroom. Make his bed and the other things in his room at the beginning of the story. Keep adding the things he puts into his room. When do you run out of room? Could you sleep there?

PreK–Grade 2
Attributes, Classification, & Patterns

What if the boy had wanted a desert lizard instead of a salamander? How would that change the story? What if he had wanted a lobster?

THE JACKET I WEAR IN THE SNOW

written by Shirley Neitzel

illustrated by Nancy Winslow Parker

Morrow, 1989

ISBN 0-688-08030-8

SUMMARY

A child, dressed for winter outdoors, stands with arms outstretched and tells us about the zipper that's stuck on the jacket. In cumulative rebus format, we hear about all the other pieces of clothing the child is forced to wear until Mother at last solves the problem.

PreK–Grade 1

Patterns

Look at the mittens and the socks. Which ones don't match? Draw pictures that give the child matching socks.

PreK–Grade 2

Attributes & Classification

Gather together lots of mittens, gloves, or socks. Find as many ways of grouping them as possible. Explain the reasons for your grouping to others.

K–Grade 2

Patterns

Make a stencil for mittens. Trace a line of mittens on a long strip of paper. Make a design and color the first mitten. Make the second mitten just like the first one, except for one thing. Make the third mitten with one more change. Keep going to the end of the paper. Compare your first and last mitten. Are they alike in any way?

PreK–Grade 1

Attributes & Classification

Make cutouts for each item of clothing in the book. Color them the way they are in the book. Find ways of grouping the items. Tell others the reasons for your groups.

PreK–Grade 1

Problem Solving

What is the problem here? When do we learn about the problem? Who solves it? What could the child have done to solve the problem? Who else might have helped? What if the mother had not been available?

Mrs. Toggle's Zipper

written by Robin Pulver
Illustrated by Robert W. Alley
Simon and Schuster, 1990
ISBN 0-02-775451-0

Summary

Mrs. Toggle, the teacher, got a new winter jacket for Christmas. She puts it on one cold winter morning and can't get it off because the zipper's stuck. Not only that, but the thing-a-ma-jig that you use to open the zipper is missing. Everybody at school gets into the act of trying to extricate Mrs. Toggle, but it's the custodian who finally does it.

Grades 1–2
Numeration

How many children do you think are in Mrs. Toggle's class? How many of their names do we learn?

Grade 2
Computation

If each child in the class wears boots to school, how many boots must be in the back of the room?

K–Grade 1
Numeration

How many people try to get Mrs. Toggle's coat off? How many different names do we learn for the pull-tab on the zipper? What is it really called? How can you find out?

PreK–Grade 2
Data Gathering & Analyzing

Make a chart listing several ways to fasten clothes. Survey the class to see which fastener is most popular.

PreK–Grade 2
Attributes & Classification

Examine a lot of zippers. In what ways are they all alike? How are they different?

Tar Beach

written and illustrated by Faith Ringgold
Random, 1991
ISBN 0-517-58031-4

Summary

This book was inspired by a quilt made by the author. It's about a family who lives in a city apartment and often goes up on the roof on hot summer evenings. They call their roof "tar beach." While lying on a quilt on "tar beach," the girl imagines herself flying over the city and anything she flies over she owns.

PreK–K

Patterns

Look closely at the quilt as it appears on the next to the last page. Find likenesses and differences among the patterns in the quilt.

PreK–Grade 2

Patterns

Find other books about quilts such as Tony Johnston's *The Quilt Story* (Putnam, 1992. ISBN 0-399-21009-1) and Lisa Ernst's *Sam Johnson and the Blue Ribbon Quilt* (Morrow, 1983. ISBN 0-688-01517-4).

Look through these and other quilt books and describe the different patterns. Many people own quilts and make them. Ask someone to come to your class to show you different kinds of quilts. Which patterns do you like best?

PreK–Grade 2

Patterns

Use wallpaper sample books to make your own flying quilt.

PreK–Grade 1

Geometry

In the pictures of the city and the bridge in this book, you can find many different kinds of shapes. How many different shapes can you find on one page? Which page has the most shapes?

THE RELATIVES CAME

written by Cynthia Rylant
illustrated by Stephen Gammell
Simon and Schuster, 1986
ISBN 0-02-777210-1

Vinieron los parients

SRA, 1995. Available in Big Book and Small Book formats.

SUMMARY

This is a story about an old-fashioned family reunion where the relatives come from far across the mountains and pile into and around the house with love and exuberance. Gammell's illustrations are so full of humor and distinctive characters that it's hard to get around to reading Rylant's equally exuberant text.

PreK–Grade 2
Data Gathering & Analyzing

There are details in the illustrations that show that the driver of the station wagon isn't very good at it. What damage does he do? Who fixes the damage?

Grades 1–2
Numeration

Can you figure out how many people are at the house? Be careful because some characters appear only once and others are on several pages.

PreK–Grade 2
Data Gathering & Analyzing

Look carefully at the boy in the blue-striped shirt who is coming out to greet the people when the car first pulls into the yard. Now find him on the next page. What's different about him? How could that have happened? Could the illustrator have made a mistake?

PreK–Grade 2
Data Gathering, Analyzing, & Patterns

Make a chart showing as many different patterns on clothing as you can find.

Patterns	How Many?
Solid Colors	▦ ▦ ▦
Flowers	▦ ▦
Stripes	▦ ▦ ▦ ▦
Plaids	▦ ▦
Checks	▦ ▦ ▦

Make small squares of each kind of pattern using wrapping paper or wallpaper. Let each group take one pattern and search each page for an example of it. Each time you find your pattern on a page, put it in the second column next to that pattern name. Which patterns appear most frequently?

PreK–Grade 2
Time & Estimation

How far away do you think the relatives lived? What makes you think so? How far have you traveled in a car? How long do you think the relatives stayed? What makes you think so?

TRAIN SONG

written by Diane Siebert
illustrated by Mike Wimmer
HarperCollins, 1990
ISBN 0-690-04728-2

SUMMARY

Here we take a poetic look at the sights and sounds of trains—all kinds of trains. The illustrations give us different perspectives of the trains with interesting and powerful pictures.

Grades 1–2

Numeration, Attributes, & Classification

How many different kinds of trains do we see in the book? How many of them have you seen in reality?

K–Grade 2

Numeration, Attributes, & Classification

Make a list of the sound words in the book. Make other lists of color words, shape words, and moving words. Which list is longest? Which is shortest?

K–Grade 2

Attributes & Classification

Find likenesses and differences among books about trains, such as Donald Crews's *Freight Train* (Morrow, 1978. ISBN 0-688-80165-X), Paul Goble's *Death of the Iron Horse* (Simon and Schuster, 1987. ISBN 0-02-737830-6), Chris Van Allsburg's *The Polar Express* (Houghton, 1985. ISBN 0-395-38949-6), and Kim Lewis's *The Last Train* (Candlewick, 1994. ISBN 1-56402-343-5).

THE MUD FLAT OLYMPICS

written and illustrated by James Stevenson
Morrow, 1994
ISBN 0-688-12823-4

SUMMARY

The animals are having their own Olympics and Stevenson presents their efforts in a mock serious tone. We begin with the carrying of the torch by Burbank. There are three contestants for the Deepest Hole contest, although one elderly mole, Mr. Crenshaw, gives up early. Hardest on the judges is the Smelliest Skunk contest, but they stay the course and rate each on a scale of one to ten. Many of the math activities in this delightful book are obvious but should be kept at the same level of enjoyment that the book projects.

Data Gathering & Analyzing

What evidence is there in the first contest that any digging was done? What evidence is there that the two contestants dug deeply? What evidence is there that they went as far as they said they did? What evidence could there have been? What would you have awarded them prizes for?

In the second contest, what evidence is there that the snails went over the hurdles? What evidence is there that they reached the finish line? What evidence could there have been?

Data Gathering & Analyzing

What do you think happened when Sid disappeared at the top of the hurdle?

Estimation

Look at the snail hurdles and the size of the animals. Find an object in your classroom that you think is about as high as the hurdles are.

Attributes & Classification

Make a list of the different animals in the book. (You might have to guess what some of them are.) Then list the special skills each animal would have. Make up some Olympic contests in which they would do well and others in which they would probably not do well.

Estimation & Computation

Read the poem "Ants at the Olympics" in the anthology *The Random House Book of Poetry for Children* (Random House, 1983. ISBN 0-394-85010-6). Compare their Olympic events to these. Would the ants have been better at the hurdles than the snails? Would they have been faster? What about the other events in the book? Which ones would the ants have failed at? Which events would take longer if you substituted the ants for one of the other animals? How long do you think the digging contest would take if the ants were the diggers?

Numeration

Which race had the most contestants? Which one had the fewest?

Numeration

At the end of the book, Crocker turns up with cookies for everybody. How many cookies should he have if everybody gets one?

Rainbow Crow

written by Nancy Van Laan
illustrated by Beatriz Vidal
Random, 1989
ISBN 0-394-89577-0

Summary

This Lenape Indian legend tells why the crow is black and has a hoarse voice. When heavy snow fell on earth and threatened to bury even the largest of animals, the animals asked the beautiful rainbow crow, who at that time had a glorious voice, to fly to the Great Sky Spirit for help. The Sky Spirit gave the crow a brand of fire to bring back to earth to melt the snow. As he carried it back, the fire scorched his feathers and ruined his voice. This is a beautiful legend, beautifully told.

PreK–K

Geometry & Spatial Sense

When the snow deepens, the smaller animals climb on top of the bigger ones. Name the animals and describe where they are in relation to each other: The bear is under the raccoon. The squirrel is on top of the wolf.

PreK–Grade 1

Measurement & Ordering

Make a list of the animals in the book. Arrange the animals from smallest to largest.

K–Grade 2

Measurement

How deep would the snow have to get before it covered the biggest animal?

Grade 2

Measurement

The Sky Spirit gave the crow fire to melt the snow. Measure some snow and then melt it. How much water do you get? Find a way to show others your results.

Grade 2

Time & Computation

The book says that the crow flew up for three days until he got to the Sky Spirit. Find out how fast a crow flies per hour and then figure out how far he could get in 72 hours. Tell us how you did it.

Grades 1–2

Attributes & Classification

Make a list of all the animals in the book. Let each group of two students choose one animal and list as many attributes as possible. Play a game of identifying the animals by their attributes.

Grades 1–2

Attributes & Classification

The book refers to "The Two-Legged One." Who do you think that is? What makes you think so? What animals would fit into that category? What about a four-legged category? A six-legged? An eight-legged? Find a way to show your results.

Alexander, Who Used to Be Rich Last Sunday

written by Judith Viorst

illustrated by Ray Cruz

Simon and Schuster, 1978

ISBN 0-689-30602-4

Alexander, Que ere rico el dominogo pasado

Simon and Schuster, 1989. ISBN 0-689-31590-2

Summary

Alexander and his two older brothers each get a dollar from their grandparents on Sunday. Alexander wants to save his money for a walkie-talkie, but he is the victim of temptation and accidental occurrences. Little by little his money goes until he is left with nothing but bus tokens.

Grades 1-2
Estimation and Money

Estimate how much money each of Alexander's brothers have on Sunday, then get the same change they have and count it.

Grade 1
Money & Computation

Change Alexander's dollar into coins in as many ways as you can.

Grade 2
Money & Computation

Use one hundred pennies and a few tokens instead of the dollar bill. As the story is read, subtract the amount of money Alexander spends. Do you end up with nothing but the tokens? What other amounts of change would have worked?

K-Grade 2
Problem Solving

Make a list of ways Alexander could have solved his problem on Sunday. Make another list of ways he could solve his problem now.

K-Grade 2
Money & Computation

Write a story about how you might spend a dollar or any sum of money.

Grades 1-2
Money & Computation

Go through catalogs of toys or other good stuff. Keep a list of the things you want along with how much each item costs. Use a calculator to figure out how much money you would spend if you bought all those things.

K-Grade 2
Probability

What do you think the chances are that Alexander will be able to save enough for a walkie-talkie?

TUESDAY

written and illustrated by David Wiesner
Houghton, 1991
ISBN 0-395-55113-7

SUMMARY

This Caldecott Award winner is almost wordless. We start before the title page as we see frogs, sitting peacefully on their lily pads, and then slowly levitating. After the title page, we join a pond turtle as he looks up in amazement. The book proper begins at sundown where text says: "Tuesday evening, around eight." The frogs start solemnly at first, and then with increasing glee they fly through the town, entering houses and startling dogs and a man enjoying a midnight snack. As dawn approaches, the pads and the frogs they bear fly lower and lower until the pads fall to earth and the frogs leap back into their pond, leaving the villagers to wonder at the lily pads left behind. The last page gives the time as "Next Tuesday, seven fifty-eight p.m." and we see shadows of flying pigs on a barn door.

PreK–K

Time

Look for clues in the book that tell you what time it is. Notice details in the illustrations, not just the printed text.

K–Grade 2

Time, Data Gathering, & Analyzing

Gather as many different kinds of timepieces as possible—working and nonworking. Don't forget sundials; hourglasses; timers; alarm clocks; stopwatches; digital and non-digital clocks and watches; wind-up, electric, and battery clocks with and without numerals on the dial; and clocks with Roman numerals. Put out 12- and 24- hour clocks. Provide tiny screwdrivers so that students can take some (preferably the nonworking ones) apart to see how they work or were supposed to work. Make charts to show their likenesses and differences.

PreK–Grade 2

Data Gathering & Analyzing

Look for evidence in the book that shows whether the power of flight comes from the frogs or the lily pads.

PreK–Grade 2

Data Gathering & Analyzing

Look at the page that shows the town in the morning. Why are the people looking puzzled? What evidence do they have that something strange happened during the night? Who could tell them what happened?

Grades 1–2

Time, Data Gathering, & Analyzing

Look out the window of your classroom. What evidence do you have about the time of day?

PreK–Grade 2

Patterns

What do you think will happen on the next Tuesday night? Why do you think so?

Section 2

Picture Books & Math Concepts Chart

Author/Title	Attributes & Classification	Patterns	Problem Solving	Numeration	Geometry & Spatial Sense	Measurement	Time	Money	Data Gathering & Analyzing	Computation	Perspective	Fractions & Proportion	Estimation	Probability
Aardema, Verna p. 118 — *Why Mosquitoes Buzz in People's Ears*		✓	✓				✓				✓			
Adams, Barbara Johnston p. 118 — *The Go-Around Dollar*								✓						
Adoff, Arnold p. 118 — *Hard to Be Six*							✓							
Ahlberg, Janet & Ahlberg, Allan p. 118 — *The Baby's Catalogue*	✓													
Allen, Pamela p. 2 — *Who Sank the Boat?*	✓	✓	✓	✓	✓	✓			✓				✓	
Altman, Linda Jacobs p. 3 — *Amelia's Road*	✓			✓	✓								✓	
Andrews, Jan p. 118 — *The Very Last First Time*							✓							
Anno, Mitsumasa p. 118 — *Anno's Alphabet*			✓								✓			
Anno, Mitsumasa p. 119 — *Anno's Counting Book*				✓			✓			✓				
Anno, Mitsumasa p. 119 — *Anno's Counting House*				✓						✓				
Anno, Mitsumasa p. 119 — *Anno's Faces*		✓		✓										
Anno, Mitsumasa p. 119 — *Anno's Flea Market*	✓								✓					
Anno, Mitsumasa p. 119 — *Anno's Hat Tricks*			✓											✓
Anno, Mitsumasa p. 119 — *Anno's Math Games*			✓							✓				✓
Anno, Mitsumasa p. 119 — *Anno's Mysterious Multiplying Jar*		✓	✓	✓						✓				
Anno, Mitsumasa p. 119 — *Anno's Sundial*						✓	✓							
Anno, Mitsumasa p. 119 — *Socrates and the Three Little Pigs*														✓
Anno, Mitsumasa p. 119 — *Topsy-Turvies*		✓	✓											✓
Anno, Mitsumasa p. 119 — *Upside Downers*			✓		✓									

Author/Title	Attributes and Classification	Patterns	Problem Solving	Numeration	Geometry & Spatial Sense	Measurement	Time	Money	Data Gathering & Analyzing	Computation	Perspective	Fractions & Proportion	Estimation	Probability
Archambault, John p. 140 *Counting Sheep*				✓										
Aylesworth, Jim p. 140 *One Crow: A Counting Rhyme*				✓						✓				
Bang, Molly p. 140 *Ten, Nine, Eight*				✓										
Barrett, Judi p. 120 *Benjamin's 365 Birthdays*			✓	✓			✓							
Barry, David p. 120 *The Rajah's Rice*		✓	✓	✓					✓	✓				
Baylor, Byrd p. 120 *Everybody Needs a Rock*	✓			✓					✓					
Baylor, Byrd p. 4 *Guess Who My Favorite Person Is*	✓	✓							✓					
Blake, Jon p. 5 *Daley B .*	✓		✓						✓					
Blundell, Tony p. 6 *Beware of Boys*	✓	✓	✓			✓	✓					✓	✓	
Brett, Jan p. 7 *The Mitten: A Ukrainian Folktale*	✓			✓	✓	✓	✓							
Brett, Jan p. 8 *Town Mouse, Country Mouse*	✓	✓	✓	✓		✓			✓	✓				
Brett, Jan p. 140 *The Twelve Days of Christmas*				✓										
Brisson, Pat p. 9 *Benny's Pennies*				✓				✓		✓				
Brown, Margaret Wise p. 121 *Goodnight Moon*		✓		✓		✓								
Brown, Margaret Wise p. 121 *The Important Book*	✓	✓												
Brown, Ruth p. 121 *A Dark Dark Tale*		✓							✓		✓			
Brown, Ruth p. 10 *The Picnic*					✓				✓		✓			
Browne, Eileen p. 11 *No Problem*	✓		✓						✓					
Bulloch, Ivan p. 121 *Games*	✓	✓		✓										✓

Author/Title	Attributes & Classification	Patterns	Problem Solving	Numeration	Geometry & Spatial Sense	Measurement	Time	Money	Data Gathering & Analyzing	Computation	Perspective	Fractions & Proportion	Estimation	Probability
Bulloch, Ivan p. 121 *Measure*						✓								
Bulloch, Ivan p. 121 *Patterns*		✓												
Bulloch, Ivan p. 121 *Shapes*					✓									
Butler, Stephen p. 12 *The Mouse and the Apple*	✓	✓		✓	✓									
Caple, Kathy p. 122 *The Purse*			✓					✓						
Carle, Eric p. 122 *The Grouchy Ladybug*						✓	✓		✓					
Carle, Eric p. 122 *Rooster's Off to See the World*		✓		✓										
Carle, Eric p. 13 *The Tiny Seed*	✓	✓			✓						✓			
Carle, Eric p. 122 *The Very Busy Spider*	✓	✓				✓	✓							
Carle, Eric p. 122 *The Very Quiet Cricket*	✓	✓					✓							
Carlstrom, Nancy p. 122 *Jesse Bear, What Will You Wear?*	✓	✓					✓							
Caseley, Judith p. 122 *Dear Annie*							✓							
Chandra, Deborah p. 140 *Miss Mabel's Table*				✓										
Charlip, Remy p. 140 *Thirteen*				✓										
Christelow, Eileen p. 140 *Five Little Monkeys*				✓										
Cleveland, David p. 122 *The April Rabbits*				✓			✓			✓			✓	✓
Cole, Brock p. 14 *The Giant's Toe*						✓							✓	
Cole, Joanna p. 15 *The Magic School Bus ... Human Body*	✓	✓		✓	✓	✓			✓	✓				
Cooney, Barbara p. 16 *Miss Rumphius*	✓	✓	✓										✓	

Author/Title	Attributes and Classification	Patterns	Problem Solving	Numeration	Geometry & Spatial Sense	Measurement	Time	Money	Data Gathering & Analyzing	Computation	Perspective	Fractions & Proportion	Estimation	Probability
Crews, Donald p. 123 *Bicycle Race*				✓										
Crews, Donald p. 123 *Freight Train*	✓			✓										
Crews, Donald p. 123 *Ten Black Dots*		✓		✓										
Crowther, Robert p. 141 *The Most Amazing Hide & Seek . . .*				✓										
de Regniers, Beatrice Schenk p. 17 *So Many Cats!*	✓	✓	✓						✓	✓		✓		
Dee, Ruby p. 123 *Two Ways to Count to Ten*			✓	✓										
DeFelice, Cynthia p. 123 *Mule Eggs*	✓		✓						✓	✓				
Derby, Sally p. 18 *The Mouse Who Owned the Sun*	✓	✓			✓				✓					
Dorros, Arthur p. 124 *Abuela*					✓						✓			
Dr. Seuss p. 19 *Yertle the Turtle and Other Stories*	✓			✓	✓	✓								
Dunrea, Olivier p. 141 *Deep Down Underground*				✓										
Dunrea, Olivier p. 20 *Eppie M. Says . . .*										✓				
Edwards, Richard p. 141 *Ten Tall Oak Trees*				✓										
Ehlert, Lois p. 141 *Fish Eyes: A Book You Can Count On*				✓										
Eichenberg, Fritz p. 141 *Dancing in the Moon: Counting Rhymes*				✓										
Emberley, Ed & Emberley, Barbara p. 124 *Drummer Hoff*		✓					✓			✓				
Emberley, Ed p. 124 *The Wing on a Flea: A Book About Shapes*					✓									
Emberley, Michael p. 124 *Welcome Back, Sun*							✓							
Everett, Percival p. 124 *The One That Got Away*				✓										

Author/Title	Attributes & Classification	Patterns	Problem Solving	Numeration	Geometry & Spatial Sense	Measurement	Time	Money	Data Gathering & Analyzing	Computation	Perspective	Fractions & Proportion	Estimation	Probability
Feelings, Muriel p. 141 *Moja Means One: A Swahili Counting Book*				✓										
Fleming, Denise p. 141 *Count!*				✓										
Fleming, Denise p. 124 *In the Tall, Tall Grass*											✓			
Fox, Mem p. 124 *Hattie and the Fox*	✓	✓							✓					✓
Fox, Mem p. 21 *Shoes from Grandpa*	✓	✓	✓	✓	✓			✓		✓				
Fox, Mem p. 125 *Time for Bed*		✓					✓							
Freschet, Berniece p. 141 *The Ants Go Marching*				✓										
Gackenbach, Dick p. 125 *King Wacky*	✓		✓								✓			
Gaffney, Michael p. 22 *Secret Forests*	✓	✓			✓									
Gammell, Stephen p. 23 *Once Upon MacDonald's Farm*	✓	✓	✓	✓					✓					
Geisert, Arthur p. 141 *Pigs from One to Ten*				✓										
George, Jean p. 125 *Dear Rebecca, Winter Is Here*							✓							
Gerstein, Mordicai p. 141 *Roll Over!*				✓										
Giganti, Paul p. 125 *Each Orange Had 8 Slices*				✓						✓		✓		
Giganti, Paul p. 125 *How Many Snails?*		✓		✓						✓				
Ginsburg, Mirra p. 125 *Across the Stream*			✓	✓										
Gollub, Matthew p. 126 *The Twenty-Five Mixtec Cats*				✓										
Greenfield, Eloise p. 126 *Africa Dream*				✓			✓							
Guiberson, Brenda p. 24 *Cactus Hotel*	✓	✓		✓			✓		✓					

Author/Title	Attributes and Classification	Patterns	Problem Solving	Numeration	Geometry & Spatial Sense	Measurement	Time	Money	Data Gathering & Analyzing	Computation	Perspective	Fractions & Proportion	Estimation	Probability
Hadithi, Mwenye p. 25 *Hungry Hyena*	✓	✓	✓							✓			✓	
Heine, Helme p. 126 *The Most Wonderful Egg in the World*	✓								✓					
Heller, Ruth p. 26 *Chickens Aren't the Only Ones*	✓	✓							✓					
Hendry, Diana p. 126 *Christmas on Exeter Street*				✓									✓	✓
Henkes, Kevin p. 27 *Chester's Way*	✓	✓	✓	✓						✓				
Henkes, Kevin p. 28 *Julius, the Baby of the World*	✓	✓		✓	✓	✓							✓	
Heuck, Sigrid p. 127 *Who Stole the Apples?*			✓											
Hill, Elizabeth Starr p. 29 *Evan's Corner*	✓		✓		✓			✓	✓	✓				
Hirst, Robin & Hirst, Sally p. 30 *My Place in Space*	✓			✓	✓	✓	✓		✓	✓				
Hoban, Lillian p. 127 *Arthur's Funny Money*								✓						
Hoban, Tana p. 127 *Circles, Triangles and Squares*	✓	✓			✓									
Hoban, Tana p. 127 *Colors Everywhere*	✓	✓												
Hoban, Tana p. 127 *Count and See*		✓		✓										
Hoban, Tana p. 127 *Dots, Spots, Speckles, and Stripes*	✓	✓												
Hoban, Tana p. 127 *Exactly the Opposite*	✓	✓												
Hoban, Tana p. 128 *Is It Larger? Is It Smaller?*	✓					✓								
Hoban, Tana p. 128 *Is It Red? Is It Yellow? Is It Blue?*	✓	✓												
Hoban, Tana p. 128 *Is It Rough? Is It Smooth? Is It Shiny?*	✓	✓												
Hoban, Tana p. 128 *Look Again!*	✓	✓									✓		✓	

Author/Title	Attributes & Classification	Patterns	Problem Solving	Numeration	Geometry & Spatial Sense	Measurement	Time	Money	Data Gathering & Analyzing	Computation	Perspective	Fractions & Proportion	Estimation	Probability
Hoban, Tana p. 128 *Look! Look! Look!*	✓	✓									✓		✓	
Hoban, Tana p. 128 *Look Up, Look Down*					✓									
Hoban, Tana p. 128 *Over, Under and Through*					✓									
Hoban, Tana p. 128 *Round and Round and Round*					✓									
Hoban, Tana p. 128 *Shapes, Shapes, Shapes*		✓			✓									
Hoban, Tana p. 128 *Spirals, Curves, Fanshapes, and Lines*		✓			✓									
Hoban, Tana p. 128 *Twenty-Six Letters and Ninety-Nine Cents*	✓			✓				✓		✓				
Hoberman, Mary Ann p. 31 *A House Is a House for Me*	✓	✓		✓					✓					
Hopkinson, Deborah p. 129 *Sweet Clara and the Freedom Quilt*		✓			✓									
Hort, Lenny p. 129 *How Many Stars in the Sky?*		✓		✓										
Hughes, Shirley p. 32 *Alfie Gets in First*	✓		✓	✓	✓					✓				
Hurd, Edith Thatcher p. 129 *Wilson's World*			✓							✓				
Hutchins, Pat p. 129 *Clocks and More Clocks*			✓				✓							
Hutchins, Pat p. 129 *Don't Forget the Bacon!*		✓						✓						
Hutchins, Pat p. 33 *The Doorbell Rang*		✓								✓			✓	
Hutchins, Pat p. 129 *Rosie's Walk*		✓			✓						✓			✓
Inkpen, Mick p. 130 *One Bear at Bedtime*		✓		✓						✓				
Johnson, Paul Brett p. 130 *The Cow Who Wouldn't Come Down*			✓											
Johnston, Tony p. 130 *Farmer Mack Measures His Pig*	✓					✓				✓				

Author/Title	Attributes and Classification	Patterns	Problem Solving	Numeration	Geometry & Spatial Sense	Measurement	Time	Money	Data Gathering & Analyzing	Computation	Perspective	Fractions & Proportion	Estimation	Probability
Johnston, Tony p. 34 — *Yonder*		✓			✓		✓		✓				✓	
Jonas, Ann p. 35 — *Reflections*	✓	✓			✓						✓			
Jonas, Ann p. 130 — *Round Trip*		✓									✓			
Kalan, Robert p. 36 — *Jump, Frog, Jump!*		✓			✓				✓					
Kimmel, Eric p. 130 — *Four Dollars and Fifty Cents*								✓						
Kitchen, Bert p. 130 — *Animal Numbers*	✓			✓										
Koller, Jackie French p. 37 — *Fish Fry Tonight*	✓		✓			✓			✓			✓		
Koscielniak, Bruce p. 131 — *Bear and Bunny Grow Tomatoes*			✓	✓										
Kraus, Robert p. 131 — *Where Are You Going, Little Mouse?*			✓		✓									
Lillegard, Dee p. 38 — *Sitting in My Box*		✓		✓	✓					✓				
Lillie, Patricia p. 39 — *When This Box Is Full*	✓			✓	✓		✓							
Lindbergh, Reeve p. 142 — *Midnight Farm*				✓										
Lionni, Leo p. 131 — *The Biggest House in the World*						✓								
Lionni, Leo p. 131 — *Inch by Inch*						✓								
Lobel, Arnold p. 40 — *Frog and Toad Are Friends*	✓				✓	✓								
Lobel, Arnold p. 131 — *Owl at Home*	✓					✓	✓							
Lobel, Arnold p. 131 — *The Rose in My Garden*		✓			✓									
London, Jonathan p. 132 — *Voices of the Wild*											✓			
Loomis, Christine p. 142 — *One Cow Coughs*				✓										

Author/Title	Attributes & Classification	Patterns	Problem Solving	Numeration	Geometry & Spatial Sense	Measurement	Time	Money	Data Gathering & Analyzing	Computation	Perspective	Fractions & Proportion	Estimation	Probability
Maestro, Betsy & Maestro, Giulio p. 132 *Dollars and Cents for Harriet*								✓						
Martin, Bill Jr & Archambault, John p. 41 *Chicka Chicka Boom Boom*	✓	✓		✓	✓	✓								
Mazer, Anne p. 42 *The Salamander Room*		✓	✓		✓	✓								
McFarlane, Sheryl p. 132 *Waiting for the Whales*		✓					✓							
McMillan, Bruce p. 132 *Beach Ball—Left, Right*		✓			✓									
McMillan, Bruce p. 132 *Becca Backward, Becca Frontward*	✓	✓												
McMillan, Bruce p. 132 *Counting Wildflowers*	✓			✓										
McMillan, Bruce p. 132 *Dry or Wet*	✓													
McMillan, Bruce p. 132 *Eating Fractions*		✓										✓		
McMillan, Bruce p. 133 *Fire Engine Shapes*		✓			✓									
McMillan, Bruce p. 133 *Mouse Views: What the Class Pet Saw*									✓		✓			
McMillan, Bruce p. 133 *One Two One Pair*		✓		✓	✓									
McMillan, Bruce p. 133 *Step by Step*				✓		✓	✓							
McMillan, Bruce p. 133 *Time to . . .*						✓	✓							
Micklethwait, Lucy p. 142 *I Spy Two Eyes: Numbers in Art*				✓										
Morris, Ann p. 133 *Hats, Hats, Hats*	✓													
Neitzel, Shirley p. 43 *The Jacket I Wear in the Snow*	✓	✓	✓											
Numeroff, Laura Joffe p. 133 *If You Give a Mouse a Cookie*		✓	✓											
O'Brien, Mary p. 142 *Counting Sheep to Sleep*				✓										

Author/Title	Attributes and Classification	Patterns	Problem Solving	Numeration	Geometry & Spatial Sense	Measurement	Time	Money	Data Gathering & Analyzing	Computation	Perspective	Fractions & Proportion	Estimation	Probability
O'Keefe, Susan Heyboer p. 133 *One Hungry Monster*			✓	✓						✓				
Parnall, Peter p. 133 *Feet!*	✓													
Philpot, Lorna & Philpot, Graham p. 142 *Amazing Anthony Ant*				✓										
Pinczes, Elinor p. 134 *One Hundred Hungry Ants*			✓	✓						✓				
Podwal, Mark p. 134 *The Book of Tens*		✓		✓										
Pulver, Robin p. 44 *Mrs. Toggle's Zipper*	✓		✓	✓					✓	✓				
Reiss, John J. p. 134 *Numbers*	✓	✓		✓	✓									
Ringgold, Faith p. 45 *Tar Beach*		✓			✓									
Ryan, Pam Muñoz p. 142 *One Hundred Is a Family*				✓										
Rylant, Cynthia p. 46 *The Relatives Came*	✓	✓		✓			✓		✓	✓			✓	
Schwartz, David M. p. 134 *How Much Is a Million?*				✓						✓				
Schwartz, David M. p. 134 *If You Made a Million*				✓				✓						
Sendak, Maurice p. 134 *Chicken Soup with Rice*		✓					✓							
Sendak, Maurice p.134 *Where the Wild Things Are*							✓							
Shulevitz, Uri p. 135 *One Monday Morning*		✓		✓			✓							
Siebert, Diane p. 47 *Train Song*	✓	✓		✓										
Sis, Peter p. 135 *Going Up! A Color Counting Book*	✓	✓		✓										
Sloat, Teri p. 135 *From One to One Hundred*				✓						✓				
Spier, Peter p. 135 *Crash! Bang! Boom!*	✓													

Author/Title	Attributes & Classification	Patterns	Problem Solving	Numeration	Geometry & Spatial Sense	Measurement	Time	Money	Data Gathering & Analyzing	Computation	Perspective	Fractions & Proportion	Estimation	Probability
Spier, Peter p. 135 *Fast-Slow High-Low: A Book of Opposites*	✓			✓										
Spier, Peter p. 135 *Gobble, Grunt, Growl*	✓													
Spier, Peter p. 135 *People*	✓													
Spier, Peter p. 135 *Peter Spier's Rain*	✓				✓									
Spier, Peter p. 135 *Tin Lizzie*							✓							
Stevenson, James p. 47 *The Mud Flat Olympics*	✓	✓	✓	✓					✓	✓			✓	
Tafuri, Nancy p. 143 *Who's Counting?*				✓										
Van Allsburg, Chris p. 136 *The Garden of Abdul Gasazi*			✓						✓					
Van Allsburg, Chris p. 136 *Two Bad Ants*											✓			
Van Laan, Nancy p. 49 *Rainbow Crow*	✓	✓			✓	✓	✓							
Van Leeuwen, Jean p. 136 *Emma Bean*							✓		✓					
Viorst, Judith p. 50 *Alexander, Who Used to Be Rich* ...			✓	✓			✓	✓		✓			✓	✓
Walsh, Ellen Stoll p. 143 *Mouse Count*				✓										
Wells, Rosemary p. 136 *Waiting for the Evening Star*		✓					✓							
Wiesner, David p. 51 *Tuesday*		✓	✓				✓		✓					
Williams, Vera p. 136 *A Chair for My Mother*			✓					✓		✓				
Wise, William p. 143 *Ten Sly Piranhas*				✓										
Wood, Audrey p. 136 *The Napping House*	✓	✓				✓	✓							
Wormell, Christopher p. 143 *A Number of Animals*				✓										

Author/Title	Attributes and Classification	Patterns	Problem Solving	Numeration	Geometry & Spatial Sense	Measurement	Time	Money	Data Gathering & Analyzing	Computation	Perspective	Fractions & Proportion	Estimation	Probability
Young, Ed p. 137 *Seven Blind Mice*	✓			✓			✓		✓		✓			
Zemach, Harve p. 137 *The Judge: An Untrue Tale*	✓	✓							✓					
Zolotow, Charlotte p. 137 *Mister Rabbit and the Lovely Present*	✓													

Section 3

Math Concept Categories

Attributes & Classification

Attributes are all of the qualities of an object that distinguish it from something else: its shape, size, weight, texture, color, and so on. As children explore and notice the attributes of an object, they learn to look at more than one quality of an object, and in combination with the knowledge that objects can be classified according to a common attribute, children recognize various patterns. With confidence in their ability to define attributes and classify objects, they can approach problems armed with many skills that will help them characterize and solve the problems.

Developmental Stages

In PreK, children are introduced to the concept of attributes with lots of opportunity for free exploration of a wide range of materials.

In kindergarten, children become more precise in their exploration and identification of attributes. Plenty of time for exploring and discussing the properties encourages children to distinguish various objects by their attributes and to communicate their thinking with others. Kindergartners can begin classification by sorting a wide variety of objects by various attributes.

First- and second-grade students become more adept at discovering attributes and describing them to others. They can subgroup by attributes and classify objects according to multiple attributes.

Using Picture Books for Attributes & Classification

Picture books provide one more opportunity for noticing and discussing attributes of people, objects, and animals. Classification activities grow naturally out of many attribute activities. In addition, attributes and their classification are used extensively in Data Gathering & Analyzing.

Attribute & Classification Activities

PreK–Grade 2

List and categorize attributes of various characters within the book. Compare them to characters in other books.

Grades 1–2

Compare the plots of a variety of books. "What attribute would you use to describe a book's plot? How is it like other books? How is it different? What other books in our class share this attribute?"

PreK–Grade 2

Describe the attributes of items in the illustrations. Compare similar items. Compare the illustrations in books about the same topic.

PreK–Grade 2

You can also use the physical look of the book itself for classification activities: "Let's take all the very tall books and put them on this shelf." Even better: "How can we arrange these books so that we can find the ones we're looking for?"

PreK–Grade 2

Ask children to rearrange the classroom library any way they think will work well and then tell others what system they used. Repeat this activity frequently. As a small group activity it necessitates conversation about the books, and it often helps children discover books they didn't know were there. The numerous classification schemes will amaze you, and the children's ability to find books based on these schemes is remarkable.

ATTRIBUTES & CLASSIFICATION

PICTURE BOOKS FOR ATTRIBUTES & CLASSIFICATION

Ahlberg, Janet and Ahlberg, Allan. *The Baby's Catalogue*. Little, 1983. ISBN 0-316-02037-0
We look at items in the young child's world in a series of categories.

Altman, Linda Jacobs. *Amelia's Road*. Illustrated by Enrique O. Sanchez. Lee & Low Books, 1993. ISBN 1-880000-04-0
Amelia hates roads and maps because her family travels to pick crops and, whenever her father takes out the map, she knows they will soon move on. How many different kinds of roads are there? (See page 3.)

Anno, Mitsumasa. *Anno's Flea Market*. Putnam, 1984. ISBN 0-399-21031-8
At this flea market, items are grouped by categories; however, it is sometimes a puzzle to figure out the rule.

Baylor, Byrd. *Everybody Needs a Rock*. Illustrated by Peter Parnall. Simon and Schuster, 1974. ISBN 0-684-13899-9 Audiocassette from Southwest Series.
In beautiful prose the author enumerates ten rules for choosing your own personal rock. In so doing, she shows us many attributes of rocks.

Baylor, Byrd. *Guess Who My Favorite Person Is*. Illustrated by Robert Andrew Parker. Simon and Schuster, 1992. ISBN 0-684-19514-3
The narrator joins a girl in her game called "tell-what-your-favorite-thing-is." What's your favorite color? Sound? (See page 4.)

Blake, Jon. *Daley B*. Illustrated by Axel Scheffter. Candlewick Press, 1992. ISBN 1-56402-078-9
While we watch Daley learn who and what he is, we discover the attributes of rabbits and weasels. (See page 5.)

Brett, Jan *The Mitten: A Ukrainian Folktale*. Putnam, 1990. ISBN 0-399-21920-X
El mitón. SRA, 1995. Available in Big Book and Small Book formats. Audiocassette from Scholastic.
Many animals enter the mitten and can be classified in several ways. (See page 7.)

Brisson, Pat. *Benny's Pennies*. Illustrated by Bob Barner. Doubleday, 1993. ISBN 0-385-41602-4
Benny buys gifts for everyone with his pennies. These gifts can be classified. (See page 9.)

Brown, Margaret Wise. *The Important Book*. Illustrated by Leonard Weisgard. HarperCollins, 1949. ISBN 0-06-020721-3
The pattern of listing attributes is the same throughout the book.

Cooney, Barbara. *Miss Rumphius*. Penguin USA, 1982. ISBN 0-670-47958-6 Audiocassette from Kimbo.
La Señorita Emilia. Spanish from Lectorum.
Miss Rumphius accomplishes her three tasks in life and the opportunity for classifying those tasks is apparent. (See page 16.)

Fox, Mem. *Hattie and the Fox*. Simon and Schuster, 1988. ISBN 0-02-735470-9
Hattie, the hen, sees an animal hiding in the bushes and proceeds to name the parts of the animal as she warns the barnyard animals. As she names each body part, we get a chance to use attributes to figure out what animal could be hiding.

Fox, Mem. *Shoes from Grandpa*. Illustrated by Patricia Mullins. Orchard, 1990. ISBN 0-531-08448-5
In this cumulative tale, each of Jessie's relatives buys her clothing to go with the shoes from Grandpa. Illustrated with cut-paper collage, Jessie's costume becomes more elaborate. (See page 21.)

Attributes & Classification

Gackenbach, Dick. *King Wacky*. Random, 1984.
ISBN 0-517-55265-5
King Wacky does everything backwards: he sits on a table and eats from a chair, he pays taxes to his people, and he says the opposite of what he means. Everything is fine until he tells the princess from another kingdom that she is the ugliest person he's ever seen. This book has attributes galore and inspiration to turn everything to its opposite.

Heller, Ruth. *Chickens Aren't the Only Ones*. Putnam, 1981. ISBN 0-448-01872-1
Las gallinas no son las únicas. Spanish from Lectorum.
In this strikingly illustrated nonfiction book about egg layers, we see domestic birds, wild birds, insects, and dinosaurs. (See page 26.)

Henkes, Kevin. *Julius, the Baby of the World*. Morrow, 1990. ISBN 0-688-09700-6
Julius, el rey de la casa. Spanish from Lectorum.
Her parents think Julius has one set of attributes, but Lilly sees a different set. (See page 28.)

Hoban, Tana. *Is It Larger? Is It Smaller?* Morrow, 1985. ISBN 0-688-04028-4
In this book of photos, the questions are implied, not stated.

Hoban, Tana. *Is It Red? Is It Yellow? Is It Blue?* Morrow, 1978. ISBN 0-688-84171-6
As the title implies, color is the system for classifying. The question is asked wordlessly by the colored circles at the bottom of the pages.

Hoban, Tana. *Is It Rough? Is It Smooth? Is It Shiny?* Morrow, 1984. ISBN 0-688-03824-7
Texture is the classification system in this book with full-color photographs that seem to invite us to touch.

Hoberman, Mary Ann. *A House Is a House for Me*. Illustrated by Betty Fraser. Penguin USA, 1978. ISBN 0-670-38016-4 Audiocassette from Live Oak.
A rhythmic text matches creatures with homes, starting out logically and getting a little zanier. (See page 31.)

Hughes, Shirley. *Alfie Gets in First*. Morrow, 1982. ISBN 0-688-00849-6
As neighbors gather to help Alfie unlock the door, we get a chance to classify them. (See page 32.)

Jonas, Ann. *Reflections*. Morrow, 1987. ISBN 0-688-06141-9
We go through a day, looking at the illustrations from two directions. (See page 35.)

Lillie, Patricia. *When This Box Is Full*. Illustrated by Donald Crews. Morrow, 1993. ISBN 0-688-12017-2
Each month we have new items to put in the box. (See page 39.)

Lobel, Arnold. *Frog and Toad Are Friends*. HarperCollins, 1970. ISBN 0-06-023958-1 Audiocassette from HarperCollins.
Sapo y sepo son amigos. Spanish from Lectorum.
Many of the stories in this easy-to-read book stress attributes and classifying, but "The Lost Button" is particularly strong. (See page 40.)

Lobel, Arnold. *Owl at Home*. HarperCollins, 1975. ISBN 0-06-023949-2 Audiocassette from HarperCollins.
This easy-to-read book has several stories, and "Tear Water Tea" is especially good for classifying activities.

McMillan, Bruce. *Dry or Wet*. Morrow, 1988. ISBN 0-688-07100-7
Concepts are presented on facing pages as seen through the antics of children.

Morris, Ann. *Hats, Hats, Hats.* Morrow, 1989.
Photographs by Ken Heyman. ISBN 0-688-06339-X
Photographs of hats make this book good for naming attributes and sorting.

Parnall, Peter. *Feet!* Simon and Schuster, 1988.
ISBN 0-02-770110-7
We take a close look at the feet of various animals, and the illustrations with the text give us things to sort and words to describe them.

Rylant, Cynthia. *The Relatives Came.* Illustrated by Stephen Gammell. Simon and Schuster, 1986.
ISBN 0-02-777210-1
Vinieron los parients. SRA, 1995. Available in Big Book and Small Book formats.
This old-fashioned family reunion of relatives galore wearing all kinds of clothes gives us many opportunities to look at attributes and classify.
[See page 46.]

Siebert, Diane. *Train Song.* Illustrated by Mike Wimmer. HarperCollins, 1990. ISBN 0-690-04728-2
The sights and sounds of trains are depicted in poetic prose and unusual perspectives.
[See page 47.]

Spier, Peter. *People.* Doubleday, 1980.
ISBN 0-385-24469-X
These oversized pages are full of people from all over the world already sorted Spier's way.

Wood, Audrey. *The Napping House.* Illustrated by Don Wood. Harcourt, 1991. ISBN 0-15-256708-9
Audiocassette from Weston Woods.
As the nappers pile up on the bed, we get a chance to see their attributes and classify them.

Young, Ed. *Seven Blind Mice.* Putnam, 1992.
ISBN 0-399-22261-8
Each of seven blind mice sees one part of the elephant and, based on that limited information, identifies it incorrectly.

PATTERNS

The ability to recognize, compare, and manipulate patterns is the basis for understanding much of mathematics. Patterns include the linear ABAB patterns that we generally think of first, as well as non-linear patterns, such as concentric, grid, and branching patterns.

Understanding the concept of patterns and being able to recognize and repeat them helps children understand such things as why a computation method works (or doesn't work) with all numbers in the same way and why one side of a triangle always has a relationship to the other two.

In problem solving, facility with patterns enables children to see the important information in a real-world math problem, how the various pieces of information relate to each other, and the possibilities for predicting the outcome.

DEVELOPMENTAL STAGES

PreK students are ready for an introduction to the idea of patterns and simple examples of patterns. They already recognize many patterns in their lives, such as those in daily routines, getting dressed, setting the table, and preparing simple foods.

In kindergarten, students can find patterns in a wide variety of contexts. They can describe the patterns to others, extend patterns, and represent patterns using cubes or other manipulatives.

In first grade, students continue to gain expertise in recognizing complex patterns and creating their own patterns.

By second grade, students can identify increasingly complex patterns in many settings and can represent and manipulate those patterns in a variety of ways.

USING PICTURE BOOKS FOR PATTERNS

The language and illustrations in picture books abound with patterns. There are so many books available today with strong or obvious patterns that listing them could fill another book. However, we've listed some of the best in this chapter. In addtion, books and activities in the chapter on Data Gathering & Analysis often involve working with patterns.

PATTERN ACTIVITIES

PreK–Grade 2

Some books have a subtle pattern. The pattern of threes, for instance, is prevalent in many folktales and in many other books with a folktale quality. There are three pigs, three bears, and three billy goats. Often there are three tasks that must be accomplished. Encourage children to find these patterns.

PreK–Grade 2

In books with an obvious language pattern, it is often useful to put the text on an overhead or on charts. Children can often see the pattern of the words even before they can actually read them, especially if the text is familiar. Using different colors for repeated words or phrases can help them identify the pattern.

K–Grade 2

Write the repeated lines from a story or poem on sentence strips and let the children reassemble the story or poem.

Patterns

K–Grade 2

Use rebuses to replace some of the words in patterned phrases. Encourage children to make their own rebuses.

PreK–Grade 2

Compare the patterns in human-made objects with patterns in natural objects. Represent some of the patterns with manipulatives.

Picture Books for Patterns

Aardema, Verna. *Why Mosquitoes Buzz in People's Ears.* Illustrated by Leo and Diane Dillon. Penguin USA, 1975. ISBN 0-8037-6087-6 Audiocassette from Weston Woods.
This African tale uses the cumulative format. A mosquito says something foolish to the iguana who puts sticks in his ears so that he will hear no more such foolishness, causing a chain of events.

Allen, Pamela. *Who Sank the Boat?* Putnam, 1990. ISBN 0-698-20679-7
¿Quién hundió el bote? SRA, 1995. Available in Big Book and Small Book formats.
A cow, a pig, a sheep, and a mouse enter a boat from biggest to smallest. Each passenger tips the boat and causes it to sit lower in the water. The question is repeated and answered after each animal gets into the boat. (See page 2.)

Brett, Jan. *Town Mouse, Country Mouse.* Putnam, 1994. ISBN 0-399-22622-2
This rendition of the common folktale contrasts two lifestyles and the pattern is clear. (See page 8.)

Brown, Margaret Wise. *Goodnight Moon.* Illustrated by Clement Hurd. HarperCollins, 1947. ISBN 0-06-020706-X Audiocassette from Live Oak.
Buenas noches luna. Spanish from Lectorum.
This classic has been around so long that we tend to take it for granted, but the repetitive text that exactly fits the pictures makes it an ideal pattern book. Many of the children will already know the words.

Brown, Margaret Wise. *The Important Book.* Illustrated by Leonard Weisgard. HarperCollins, 1949. ISBN 0-06-020721-3
The pattern of attributes is the same throughout the book.

Brown, Ruth. *A Dark Dark Tale.* Penguin USA, 1981. ISBN 0-8037-0093-8 Audiocassette from Weston Woods.
This is a funny tale of a dark, dark night and a dark, dark visitor to a dark, dark house. Read it aloud in your spookiest voice—but whisper or squeak the ending.

Bulloch, Ivan. *Patterns.* Thomson, 1994. ISBN 1-56847-230-7
This book is one of a series called "Action Math" and presents activities for young children who are investigating patterns.

Butler, Stephen. *The Mouse and the Apple.* Morrow, 1994. ISBN 0-688-12811-4
A mouse is joined by other animals as he sits under a tree waiting for an apple to drop. The pattern of moving animals is obvious. (See page 12.)

Carle, Eric. *Rooster's Off to See the World.* Picture Book Studios, 1991. ISBN 0-88708-042-1
The pattern of animals joining and leaving the procession is similar to that in many folktales.

Carle, Eric. *The Tiny Seed.* Picture Book Studio, 1991. ISBN 0-88708-015-4
It's fall and the seeds are being blown along by the wind. One tiny seed survives to flower and scatter its seeds to the wind. (See page 13.)

Carle, Eric. *The Very Busy Spider*. Putnam, 1989.
ISBN 0-399-21592-1
This delightfully simple book is as pleasant to touch as it is to view. The spider's web and the fly are raised from the page. This, combined with its repetitive text, should make it a favorite with the very young.

Carle, Eric. *The Very Quiet Cricket*. Putnam, 1990.
ISBN 0 399-21885-8
As other insects pass him, making their unique sounds, a very small cricket tries again and again to chirp by rubbing his wings together. Each time a patterned sequence follows.

Carlstrom, Nancy. *Jesse Bear, What Will You Wear?* Illustrated by Bruce Degen. Simon and Schuster, 1986. ISBN 0-02-717350-X
This favorite is a rhyming text of repeated questions and phrases and is full of exuberant silliness.

Cooney, Barbara. *Miss Rumphius*. Penguin USA, 1982.
ISBN 0-670-47958-6 Audiocassette from Kimbo.
La Señorita Emilia. Spanish from Lectorum.
Patterning her life after her grandfather's, Miss Rumphius has three goals: to travel the world, to retire by the sea, and to leave the world more beautiful. (See page 16.)

de Regniers, Beatrice Schenk. *So Many Cats!* Illustrated by Ellen Weiss. Houghton, 1985.
ISBN 0-89919-700-0
As each cat becomes part of the household, we recount the others. The repetitive text is charming. (See page 17.)

Emberley, Ed and Emberley, Barbara. *Drummer Hoff*. Simon and Schuster, 1985. ISBN 0-671-66682-7
Soldiers build a cannon and fire it, whereupon it explodes. Rhythmic text and rhyme with striking woodcuts tell the story.

Fox, Mem. *Hattie and the Fox*. Illustrated by Patricia Mullins. Simon and Schuster, 1988.
ISBN 0-02-735470-9
This is a little bit like "The Little Red Hen" in that no one cares what a hen does or, in this case, what she sees. Each animal has a suitably disdainful reply to each observation she makes—until the fox springs out. These remarks form the basis for the predictable repetition.

Fox, Mem. *Shoes from Grandpa*. Illustrated by Patricia Mullins. Orchard, 1990. ISBN 0-531-08448-5
In this cumulative tale, each of Jessie's relatives buys her an article of clothing to go with the shoes her Grandpa bought her. Illustrated with cut-paper collage, the book is light and playful as Jessie's costume gets more and more elaborate.
(See page 21.)

Guiberson, Brenda. *Cactus Hotel*. Illustrated by Megan Lloyd. Henry Holt, 1991. ISBN 0-8050-1333-4
We examine the ecology of a desert by observing the life cycle of a giant cactus. (See page 24.)

Heller, Ruth. *Chickens Aren't the Only Ones*. Putnam, 1981. ISBN 0-448-01872-1
Las gallinas no son las únicas. Spanish from Lectorum.
In this strikingly illustrated nonfiction book about egg layers, we see domestic birds, wild birds, insects, and dinosaurs. (See page 26.)

Henkes, Kevin. *Chester's Way*. Morrow, 1988.
ISBN 0-688-07608-4
Chester, un tipo con personalidad. SRA, 1995.
Available in Lap Book and Small Book formats.
Chester and Wilson are good friends and very much alike. The story pattern stresses their likenesses. (See page 27.)

PATTERNS

Hoban, Tana. *Dots, Spots, Speckles, and Stripes.* Morrow, 1987. ISBN 0-688-06862-6
Vivid photographs wordlessly illustrate patterns in feathers, flowers, people, and animals.

Hoban, Tana. *Exactly the Opposite.* Morrow, 1990. ISBN 0-688-08862-7
As in other opposite books, the ABAB pattern is clear. From Hoban's typically vivid photographs we learn vocabulary as well as pattern.

Hoberman, Mary Ann. *A House Is a House for Me.* Illustrated by Betty Fraser. Penguin USA, 1978. ISBN 0-670-38016-4 Audiocassette from Live Oak.
A rhythmic text matches creatures with homes, starting out logically and getting a little zanier. The title is the repeated phrase. [See page 31.]

Hopkinson, Deborah. *Sweet Clara and the Freedom Quilt.* Illustrated by James Ransome. Random, 1993. ISBN 0-679-82311-5
A young slave stitches a quilt with a map pattern that will lead her to freedom.

Hutchins, Pat. *Don't Forget the Bacon!* Morrow, 1978. ISBN 0-688-06788-3 Audiocassette from Live Oak.
His mother sends him to the store for "Six farm eggs,/a cake for tea,/a pound of pears,/and don't forget the bacon." Chanting as he goes it becomes "Six clothes pegs,/a rake for leaves,/and a pile of chairs," but he forgets the bacon. Following his chant and making your own by changing the shopping list are pattern activities.

Hutchins, Pat. *The Doorbell Rang.* Morrow, 1986. ISBN 0-688-05252-5
Llaman a la puerta. Spanish from Lectorum.
The story doesn't tell us how many cookies there are at the beginning, but it does tell us how many there are for each child as more and more children arrive. The patterned text repeats throughout the book. [See page 33.]

Hutchins, Pat. *Rosie's Walk.* Simon and Schuster, 1968. ISBN 0-02-745850-4 Audiocassette from Weston Woods.
Rosie, the hen, takes a leisurely walk around the barnyard, not heeding the fox whom she foils at every turn. The words are easy to read because they are all prepositional phrases that detail Rosie's walk while completely ignoring the fox, who is never mentioned in the text. The illustrations are full of unusual patterns, and predicting what will happen next to the fox brings students to the plot's pattern.

Jonas, Ann. *Reflections.* Morrow, 1987. ISBN 0-688-06141-9
We go through a day, looking at the illustrations from two directions. [See page 35.]

Kalan, Robert. *Jump, Frog, Jump!* Illustrated by Byron Barton. Morrow, 1981. ISBN 0-688-09241-1
¡Salta, ranita, salta! Spanish from Lectorum.
A cumulative tale that starts with a fly and ends with a frog nearly being caught by some boys. Each new event becomes part of the repeated pattern. [See page 36.]

Koscielniak, Bruce. *Bear and Bunny Grow Tomatoes.* Random, 1993. ISBN 0-679-93687-4
Bear and Bunny both start gardens. Bear is careful to do everything right—preparing the soil and tending the plants. Bunny throws the seeds on the ground and then sits back to watch. Bunny's antics as he waits for his tomatoes are silly and make this book wonderful in spite of the standard plot. The book emphasizes sequencing.

Lillegard, Dee. *Sitting in My Box.* Illustrated by Jon Agee. Penguin USA, 1989. ISBN 0-525-44528-5
A little boy starts out alone in his box. One by one animals join and then leave him. [See page 38.]

PATTERNS

Lobel, Arnold. *The Rose in My Garden.* Illustrated by Anita Lobel. Morrow, 1984. ISBN 0-688-02587-0
Using their combined skills, Arnold and Anita Lobel tell of a simple incident in a garden. The words will stretch the imagination and the illustrations will delight the eye.

Martin, Bill Jr and Archambault, John. *Chicka Chicka Boom Boom.* Illustrated by Lois Ehlert. Simon & Schuster, 1989. ISBN 0-671-67949-X Big Book, Small Book, and audiocassette formats available from SRA.
Animated letters climb the tree in alphabetical order. The pattern is in the rhythmic chant and in the alphabetical order. [See page 41.]

McFarlane, Sheryl. *Waiting for the Whales.* Illustrated by Ron Lighburn. Putnam, 1993. ISBN 0-399-22515-3
A grandfather imparts his love of whale watching to his granddaughter as they wait for the yearly migration of the whales.

McMillan, Bruce. *Becca Backward, Becca Frontward: A Book of Concept Pairs.* Morrow, 1986. ISBN 0-688-06283-0
The ABAB pattern is clear in this book of colored photographs in which a dozen pairs of opposites are pointed out in the actions and reactions of a little girl.

McMillan, Bruce. *Step by Step.* Morrow, 1987. ISBN 0-688-07233-X
We watch a little boy moving around from the time he is four months until fourteen months old. He goes from wiggler to walker in color photographs.

Neitzel, Shirley. *The Jacket I Wear in the Snow.* Illustrated by Nancy Winslow Parker. Morrow, 1989. ISBN 0-688-08030-8
Using a "This Is the House That Jack Built" pattern, every piece of clothing is placed on the boy who can then do everything but walk. [See page 43.]

Numeroff, Laura Joffe. *If You Give a Mouse a Cookie.* HarperCollins, 1985. Illustrated by Felicia Bond. ISBN 0-06-024587-5
Each action causes another until we're back to the beginning cookie and mouse.

Ringgold, Faith. *Tar Beach.* Random, 1991. ISBN 0-517-58031-4
The pattern here is in the quilts. [See page 45.]

Sendak, Maurice. *Chicken Soup with Rice.* HarperCollins, 1962. ISBN 0-06-025535-8
Audiocassette from Weston Woods.
Sendak's ode to the seasons far precedes the current interest in pattern books, but it certainly fits the criteria.

Shulevitz, Uri. *One Monday Morning.* Simon and Schuster, 1974. ISBN 0-684-13195-1
This is a delicate story of a lonely little boy and a chain of distinguished visitors. The story also emphasizes the days of the week.

Wood, Audrey. *The Napping House.* Illustrated by Don Wood. Harcourt, 1991. ISBN 0-15-256708-9
Audiocassette from Weston Woods.
This tale builds a pile of sleeping creatures and then puts a wakeful flea at the top. The humor, vocabulary, and color make this an outstanding book.

Problem Solving

Problem solving is not just a skill used in deciphering a paragraph on a test. Problem solving is the context in which all real-world mathematics takes place. In everyday life, math is one tool we use to solve problems. Problem solving includes figuring out what the problem is, what we need to know, what we know so far, how we can approach the problem, what approach will work best for us, and whether the answers we get make sense.

According to the Curriculum and Evaluation Standards written by the National Council of Teachers of Mathematics, "Problem solving is not a distinct topic but a process that should permeate the entire program and provide the context in which concepts and skills can be learned."

When we use cooperative learning activities, constructivist math methods, and investigation-based mathematics projects, we are creating a classroom in which problem-solving experiences are bountiful and where students accumulate an ever-growing number of successes with solving problems.

Because of the overriding environmental aspect of problem solving, most of the activities in this book are about problem solving, regardless of the section in which they are listed. In addition, we found situations in picture books that deal with the idea of solving problems in general. These types of books and activities are included in this chapter on problem solving and are labeled "problem solving" in other sections of this book.

Developmental Stages

The mathematical or other skills necessary to solve a problem that you use with your students should be developmentally appropriate.

The development of problem-solving skills from PreK to second grade ranges from first learning to define problems in situation-specific terms to more generalized and inclusive understandings of the problem. Students grow in their ability to describe the problem and its solutions accurately.

By first grade students can begin to create variations on the problems presented in the stories. As students approach second grade, they can compare similar problems and approaches to problem solving in different books.

Using Picture Books for Problem Solving

Picture books provide many opportunities for class discussion and for playfulness with the idea of multiple approaches and multiple solutions to problems. "What is going on here? What is the character's main problem? How do they approach the problem? How many different ways can we think of to approach the problem? Let's list all the solutions we can think of and then go through the list to see which ones might work and which ones might not."

Problem-Solving Activities

PreK–Grade 2
Most stories involve one or more characters on a quest, and how the characters do or do not reach their goal is the gist of the story. Encourage children to identify the problem, brainstorm for divergent ways to solve it, hypothesize how this character will do it, and check their hypothesis.

Grades 1–2
Make flowcharts of the books, highlighting the point at which the problem was recognized and again the point at which it was resolved.

Problem Solving

Grades 1–2

Set the same characters on another quest. Again, state the problem you have set up and list different ways it could be solved.

Grades 1–2

Problems from a group of books can be analyzed and categorized. What causes the problem in the story? Misunderstanding? Lack of information? Lack of logic? Miscalculation? Too few or too many of something? How was the problem solved? Luck? A third party? Logical thinking? Critical thinking?

Picture Books for Problem Solving

Aardema, Verna. *Why Mosquitoes Buzz in People's Ears*. Illustrated by Leo and Diane Dillon. Penguin USA, 1975. ISBN 0-8037-6087-6 Audiocassette from Weston Woods.
The lion solves the problem by getting testimony from each of the participants.

Allen, Pamela. *Who Sank the Boat?* Putnam, 1990. ISBN 0-698-20679-7
¿Quién hundió el bote? SRA, 1995. Available in Big Book and Small Book formats.
We, the readers, are presented with the problem throughout the book. (See page 2.)

Anno, Mitsumasa. *Anno's Hat Tricks*. Putnam, 1985. ISBN 0-399-21212-4
This is a difficult puzzle for many primary children; however, some will be able to follow the binary logic quite well.

Anno, Mitsumasa. *Anno's Math Games* I, II, and III. Putnam, 1991.
Many primary children will be confused or frustrated with these three math games books, but those who can follow the games should find them delightful. The puzzles increase in difficulty throughout each book.

Blake, Jon. *Daley B.* Illustrated by Axel Scheffter. Candlewick Press, 1992. ISBN 1-56402-078-9
Daley B.'s problem is his lack of knowledge. (See page 5.)

Blundell, Tony. *Beware of Boys*. Morrow, 1992. ISBN 0-688-10925-X
The boy's problem is that he's been captured by a wolf. The wolf's problem is that the boy keeps demanding that he fetch more things. (See page 6.)

Brett, Jan. *The Mitten: A Ukrainian Folktale*. Putnam, 1990. ISBN 0-399-21920-X Audiocassette from Scholastic.
El Mitón. SRA, 1995. Available in Big Book and Small Book formats.
There are two main problems in this one: The boy needs to find his missing mitten and too many animals are taking shelter in it. (See page 7.)

Brisson, Pat. *Benny's Pennies*. Illustrated by Bob Barner. Doubleday, 1993. ISBN 0-385-41602-4
Benny has only five pennies and everyone wants something. (See page 9.)

Browne, Eileen. *No Problem*. Illustrated by David Parkins. Candlewick, 1993. ISBN 1-56402-176-9
Not only do we disagree with the title statement, we see what the problem is each time. (See page 11.)

Caple, Kathy. *The Purse*. Houghton, 1986. ISBN 0-395-41852-6
Katie faces several problems in this simple story. She identifies each problem and solves them one by one.

PROBLEM SOLVING

Cooney, Barbara. *Miss Rumphius*. Penguin USA, 1982. ISBN 0-670-47958-6 Audiocassette from Kimbo. *La Señorita Emilia*. Spanish from Lectorum. Miss Rumphius has three goals. The third one presents the biggest challenge. (See page 16.)

Dee, Ruby. *Two Ways to Count to Ten*. Henry Holt, 1988. ISBN 0-8050-0407-6 In this African folktale, Tiny Antelope solves the problem posed by the king.

DeFelice, Cynthia. *Mule Eggs*. Illustrated by Mike Shenon. Orchard, 1994. ISBN 00531-06843-9 Patrick has a problem: he is being duped by a farmer. After he realizes that he's been fooled, he has another problem: how to get even.

Fox, Mem. *Shoes from Grandpa*. Illustrated by Patricia Mullins. Orchard, 1990. ISBN 0-531-08448-5 In this cumulative tale, each of Jessie's relatives buys her clothing to go with the shoes her Grandpa bought her. Illustrated with cut-paper collage, Jessie's costume gets more and more elaborate. In the end, she begs for a pair of jeans and takes off on her skateboard. (See page 21.)

Gammell, Stephen. *Once Upon MacDonald's Farm*. Simon and Schuster, 1984. ISBN 0-02-737210-3 *Erasé una vez, en la granja del señor MacDonald*. SRA, 1995. Available in Big Book and Small Book formats. MacDonald's farm had no animals. So, he bought an elephant, a baboon, and a lion. (See page 23.)

Ginsburg, Mirra. *Across the Stream*. Illustrated by Nancy Tafuri. Morrow, 1982. ISBN 0-688-01206-X A hen and her three chicks must cross a stream to escape from the fox.

Hadithi, Mwenye. *Hungry Hyena*. Illustrated by Adrienne Kennaway. Little, 1994. ISBN 0-316-33715-3 Hungry Hyena has tricked Fish Eagle out of his meal of fish for the last time. (See page 25.)

Henkes, Kevin. *Chester's Way*. Morrow, 1988. ISBN 0-688-07608-4 *Chester, un tipo con personalidad*. SRA, 1995. Available in Lap Book and Small Book formats. When a new and unconventional child, Lilly, moves into the neighborhood, Chester and Wilson's conservative ways are threatened. (See page 27.)

Hill, Elizabeth Starr. *Evan's Corner*. Illustrated by Sandra Speidel. Penguin USA, 1991. ISBN 0-670-82830-0 Evan has a problem: He wants a place of his own, but there's not much private space when eight people live in his two-room apartment. (See page 29.)

Hughes, Shirley. *Alfie Gets in First*. Morrow, 1982. ISBN 0-688-00849-6 All the neighbors are involved in this problem of a locked door. (See page 32.)

Hurd, Edith Thacher. *Wilson's World*. Illustrated by Clement Hurd. HarperCollins, 1994. ISBN 0-06-443359-5 Wilson paints a beautiful globe. Step by step he paints the evolution of life and civilization. He ends up with an overpopulated and polluted mess. To solve his problem, he starts over, only this time he paints people who take care of the Earth.

Johnson, Paul Brett. *The Cow Who Wouldn't Come Down*. Orchard, 1993. ISBN 0-531-08631-3 The problem here is the cow up there, defying all logic and gravity.

Koller, Jackie French. *Fish Fry Tonight*. Illustrated by Catharine O'Neill. Random, 1992. ISBN 0-517-57815-8 Mouse thinks she has no problem: she's caught a big fish and invited squirrel and maybe a friend or two for a fish fry. The problem? Too many guests and too small a fish. (See page 37.)

Problem Solving

Lobel, Arnold. *Owl at Home.* HarperCollins, 1975.
ISBN 0-06-023949-2 Audiocassette from
HarperCollins.
Owl faces several problems in this delightful and
easy-to-read collection of short stories.

Mazer, Anne. *The Salamander Room.* Illustrated by
Steve Johnson. Random, 1991.
ISBN 0-394-92945-4
A boy wants to keep the salamander as a pet. His
mother keeps presenting problems this will create.
He solves each problem but not very realistically.
[See page 42.]

McMillan, Bruce. *Eating Fractions.* Scholastic, 1991.
ISBN 0-590-43770-4
Clear color photographs show two children dividing
various foods into halves, thirds, and quarters, and
then having fun eating.

Numeroff, Laura Joffe. *If You Give a Mouse a Cookie.*
HarperCollins, 1985. Illustrated by Felicia Bond.
ISBN 0-06-024587-5
Each problem is solved, but the solution causes
another problem.

Pinczes, Elinor. *One Hundred Hungry Ants.* Houghton,
1993. ISBN 0-395-63116-5
One hundred ants are rushing off to a picnic.
Unfortunately, there's one ant who keeps regrouping them.

Wiesner, David. *Tuesday.* Houghton, 1991.
ISBN 0-395-55113-7
Frogs flying on lily pads invade the village during the
night. Police and other investigators find no evi-
dence, except lily pads all over the place.
[See page 51.]

Numeration

Numeration is more complex than being able to count by rote. Numeration includes a complete understanding of a number: what that many of something look like, how that number can be grouped into subgroups, how that number is similar and different from other numbers, and what the symbol for the number looks like. Numeration and early computation skills develop hand in hand as students combine, separate, and in other ways manipulate sets or groups.

If we limit numeration development to rote counting, then we miss the deeper understanding of what these words and symbols mean. A more well-rounded immersion in the concept of each number and building a familiarity with each number pays off down the road as students do more and more complex and abstract work with numbers.

In this chapter on numeration we included one-to-one correspondence, counting, number sense, ordering, and place value. One-to-one correspondence develops as children compare sets. Number sense is an internalized concept of what the number is and how it relates to other numbers. Ordering applies to working with any sequence: life cycle, book plot, short to tall, smooth to rough, few to many. Finally, place value is our base ten system. Dealing with place value during calculations is included in the section on computation.

Developmental Stages

At the PreK level, pre-numeration work focuses on attributes, classification, patterns, ordering, and one-to-one correspondence. Extensive work on these concepts creates a solid foundation for future work in numeration. Simple ordering activities, one-to-one correspondence work, and a beginning understanding of how numerals are used to represent amounts are all part of this stage.

In Kindergarten, numeration includes a familiarity with the numbers 1–10, or in some curricula, 1–20. Manipulating objects and becoming familiar with the configurations of a number (for example, five is xx xxx, x xxxx, and xx x xx) build internal familiarity with concepts. Students in kindergarten are new at conservation of number—the regrouping of objects—and this is where much of the work takes place at this age. Kindergarten students can begin to explore how numbers can be separated into other numbers and combined to make new numbers. One-to-one correspondence and ordering concepts should be solidifying at this stage.

First graders' work with numeration includes a sense of the relative size of numbers, usually working up to 100. Becoming comfortable grouping and regrouping objects in a wide variety of ways when working with numbers is important at this stage.

By second grade, students are ready to work with higher numbers. What do these numbers mean? What does 200 of something look like? How are numbers related to each other? Looking for patterns in the attributes of numbers and how they are written develops a grounding in place value.

Using Picture Books for Numeration

There are many picture books for children designed for counting. These counting books, so as not to overwhelm other numeration books, are listed separately in Appendix A. Here we've listed books that do more than count.

Numeration Activities

K–Grade 2

Obviously many items within a book can be counted and numbers compared. You can decide without counting whether there are more of one group than another within the story and then count to check your hypothesis.

K

With younger children, placing squares of paper in columns to represent each set within the story can help them establish the concept of more or less.

K-Grade 1

Page numbers, if present, are an opportunity to discuss numeration and to estimate whether the desired page will be nearer the front or the back of a book.

K-Grade 1

If a book has a table of contents or index, both cardinal and ordinal numeration come into a conversation easily.

K-Grade 2

Look for different groupings within a number of objects: three hippos in the tub and two at the sink are five hippos.

Grades 1-2

Use counting books (see Appendix A, page 140) and other books that involve specific numbers of objects as models for students to create their own counting or number books.

Grades 1-2

Look in a variety of books for as many different groupings of a specific number as you can find. For instance, look for illustrations that show different groupings of ten: five and five, three and three and three and one, one and nine.

PICTURE BOOKS FOR NUMERATION

Allen, Pamela. *Who Sank the Boat?* Putnam, 1990. ISBN 0-698-20679-7
¿Quién hundió el bote? SRA, 1995. Available in Big Book and Small Book formats.
We can keep track of the friends who enter the boat one by one. (See page 2.)

Anno, Mitsumasa. *Anno's Counting Book.* HarperCollins, 1977. ISBN 0-690-01288-8
Against a barren landscape, Anno presents sets of numbers and their numerals, the months and seasons, and even builds us a village. There is so much to count and examine here that one look is not enough.

Anno, Mitsumasa. *Anno's Counting House.* Putnam, 1982. ISBN 0-399-20896-8
Through cut-out windows and exterior and interior views, we watch ten children move from a house on one side of the street to a house on the other. In so doing, we can count and see many combinations of ten.

Barrett, Judi. *Benjamin's 365 Birthdays.* Illustrated by Ron Barrett. Simon and Schuster, 1992. ISBN 0-689-3179-1
Benjamin loves getting presents so much that he wraps up his already opened birthday presents and unwraps one each day for a year.

Barry, David. *The Rajah's Rice.* Illustrated by Donna Perrone. Freeman, 1994. ISBN 0-7167-6568-3
Subtitled "A Mathematical Folktale from India," this book is just that. A young girl gets the Rajah to promise her rice as calculated on a chess board, doubling the previous amount on each square of the board.

Numeration

Brett, Jan. *The Mitten: A Ukrainian Folktale.* Putnam, 1990. ISBN 0-399-21920-X   Audiocassette from Scholastic.
El mitón. SRA, 1995. Available in Big Book and Small Book formats.
Animals squeeze into an ever-stretching mitten one by one. (See page 7.)

Brisson, Pat. *Benny's Pennies.* Illustrated by Bob Barner. Doubleday, 1993. ISBN 0-385-41602-4
Benny starts out with five pennies and ends up with none. (See page 9.)

Butler, Stephen. *The Mouse and the Apple.* Morrow, 1994. ISBN 0-688-12811-4
A mouse sits under an apple tree and waits for its lone ripe apple to fall. One by one, other animals join the mouse until there are five animals waiting for the apple to drop. (See page 12.)

Cleveland, David. *The April Rabbits.* Illustrated by Nurit Karlin. Scholastic, 1986. ISBN 0-590-42369-X
Each day of April, David discovers that number of rabbits in his life. This is a good counting book because the story is funny and it combines ordinal and cardinal numbers.

Crews, Donald. *Bicycle Race.* Morrow, 1985. ISBN 0-688-05172-3
Keeping track of twelve racers, with their numbers prominently displayed, puts the accent on numeral identification.

Dee, Ruby. *Two Ways to Count to Ten.* Henry Holt, 1988. ISBN 0-8050-0407-6
In this African folktale, Tiny Antelope solves the problem posed by the king: it involves counting singly and counting by two's.

Everett, Percival. *The One That Got Away.* Illustrated by Dirk Zimmer. Houghton, 1992. ISBN 0-395-52550-3
Three cowboys rustle up a herd of ones. That's right, the numerals. The laughs are in the puns: "They caught one . . . .They went looking for another one." In the end, they return to where they had left eight ones and find "not a single one," but the numeral 8.

Fox, Mem. *Shoes from Grandpa.* Illustrated by Patricia Mullins. Orchard, 1990. ISBN 0-531-08448-5
In this cumulative tale, each of Jessie's relatives buys her clothing to go with the shoes her Grandpa bought her. Illustrated with cut-paper collage, the book is light and playful as Jessie's costume becomes more and more elaborate. Jessie, of course, would much rather wear her jeans. (See page 21.)

Giganti, Paul. *How Many Snails?* Illustrated by Donald Crews. Morrow, 1988. ISBN 0-688-06370-5
As we view different sites, we are asked to count a variety of items. Then we count subsets.

Ginsburg, Mirra. *Across the Stream.* Illustrated by Nancy Tafuri. Morrow, 1982. ISBN 0-688-01206-X
A hen and her three chicks must cross a stream to escape from the fox. They are helped by a duck and three ducklings who ferry the hen and her chicks across the stream on their backs.

Gollub, Matthew. *The Twenty-Five Mixtec Cats.* Illustrated by Leovigildo Martinez. Morrow, 1993. ISBN 0-688-11640-X
The inhabitants of Oaxaca, Mexico, are not pleased with the number of cats in their healer's house.

Greenfield, Eloise. *Africa Dream.* Illustrated by Carole Byard. HarperCollins, 1989. ISBN 0-690-04776-2
A child fantasizes about the African home of her ancestors, where she imagines that her grandfather planted a seed that grew into ten mango trees for her.

Numeration

Hendry, Diana. *Christmas on Exeter Street.* Illustrated by John Lawrence. Random, 1989. ISBN 0-679-90134-5
The house is elegant and a perfect place for a picture-book Christmas. Then the relatives and the neighbors, invited and not invited, show up, and somehow they find room for all the houseguests.

Henkes, Kevin. *Chester's Way.* Morrow, 1988. ISBN 0-688-07608-4
Chester, un tipo con personalidad. SRA, 1995. Available in Lap Book and Small Book formats. Chester and Wilson have so many things in common that one-to-one correspondence is obvious here. (See page 27.)

Hirst, Robin and Hirst, Sally. *My Place in Space.* Illustrated by Roland Harvey and Joe Levine. Orchard Books, 1990. ISBN 0-531-08459-0
When a bus driver teases Henry that maybe he doesn't know his address, Henry rises to the occasion and tells the driver precisely where he lives: 12 Main Street, Gumbridge, Australia, Southern Hemisphere, Earth, solar system, solar neighborhood, Orion Arm, Milky Way Galaxy, local group of galaxies, Virgo Supercluster, the universe. The book is full of large numbers in context. (See page 30.)

Hoban, Tana. *Count and See.* Simon and Schuster, 1972. ISBN 0-02-744800-2
Hoban gives us interesting objects to count in her black-and-white photographs.

Hort, Lenny. *How Many Stars in the Sky?* Illustrated by James Ransome. Morrow, 1991. ISBN 0-688-10104-6
A father and child attempt to count the stars.

Hughes, Shirley. *Alfie Gets in First.* Morrow, 1982. ISBN 0-688-00849-6
Alfie hides behind a locked door as helpers gather outside in sets of varying size. (See page 32.)

Kitchen, Bert. *Animal Numbers.* Penguin USA, 1987. ISBN 0-8037-0459-3
Fifteen animals are shown with their offspring, and readers are asked to determine how many are in each brood.

Lillegard, Dee. *Sitting in My Box.* Illustrated by Jon Agee. Penguin USA, 1989. ISBN 0-525-44528-5
As a little boy sits in a box, when someone knocks—it's a giraffe. One by one animals enter and leave the box. The text is rhythmic with a strong pattern. (See page 38.)

Lillie, Patricia. *When This Box Is Full.* Illustrated by Donald Crews. Morrow, 1993. ISBN 0-688-12017-2
An empty box becomes a treasure of memories. Each month the child addsnew items that remind her of the the month. (See page 39.)

McMillan, Bruce. *Counting Wildflowers.* Morrow, 1986. ISBN 0-688-02860-8
We can count the wildflower blossoms in these beautiful photographs, and we are quite willing to do so. We can also concentrate on numerous properties: color, shape, and size, for instance.

McMillan, Bruce. *One Two One Pair.* Scholastic, 1991. ISBN 0-590-43767-4
First, we see the separate elements, and then two of them make a pair. There are opportunities here for left-and-right spatial relationships, patterning, and numeration.

Podwal, Mark. *The Book of Tens.* Morrow, 1994. ISBN 0-688-12994-3
This book examines the number ten as it appears in the Old Testament. Each citing of ten is accompanied by a short paragraph explaining the reference.

NUMERATION

Schwartz, David M. *How Much Is a Million?* Illustrated
by Steven Kellogg. Morrow, 1985.
ISBN 0-688-04049-7
Not only a million, but a billion and a trillion are
shown in graphic ways that help children understand these difficult concepts.

Schwartz, David M. *If You Made a Million.* Morrow,
1989. ISBN 0-688-07018-3
Starting with one dollar and proceeding to a million,
this is a wonderful book involving much more than
counting.

Young, Ed. *Seven Blind Mice.* Putnam, 1992.
ISBN 0-399-22261-8
Each of seven blind mice sees one part of an elephant and, based on that limited information, identifies it incorrectly. The mice are ordered in two
ways—by the days of the week and by ordinals.

Geometry & Spatial Sense

Geometry and Spatial Sense includes the exploration of shapes and solids and relationships such as *over, under, inside, behind, far,* and *near.* Development in this area includes the ability to describe an object according to its shape and its position. Mapping activities, which include both measuring and spatial relationships, are included in this section.

Developmental Stages

In PreK, students are introduced to simple shapes and encouraged to explore their attributes. Simple vocabulary for spatial position is modeled in the classroom and encouraged in the students.

In kindergarten, students identify simple shapes and their attributes and continue their work on describing position.

By first grade, students work with solid shapes (sphere, cube, and cylinder) and relate them to flat shapes. Mapping work involves understanding and communicating spatial relationships.

In second grade, students explore more fully the relationship between different shapes and their attributes, and their understanding of maps and mapping can really take off.

Using Picture Books for Geometry & Spatial Sense

Picture books are rich in interesting illustrations of shapes and position. While sharing a book individually or with a group, there are many opportunities to notice shape and to use spatial relationships to describe what each person sees. Books containing trips or specific geographic locations can inspire mapping activities.

Geometry & Spatial Sense Activities

PreK-Grade 2

Look through a book for various geometric shapes. How can you tell it is a triangle, a square, and so on? What makes a triangle a triangle?

PreK-Grade 2

Look through a book together for shapes. How many different shapes can you find? How many different types of each shape can you find? Discuss why an object is a particular shape and whether the shape serves a purpose. What would happen if the shape were different?

PreK-Grade 2

As you are sharing a picture book and the children are commenting and pointing out various items, encourage them to describe *where* the item is rather than pointing to it.

PreK-Grade 1

Often, the action of a book involves characters or items in various positions: The bear is inside the mitten. He's beside the hedgehog. The mouse is on top of the bear's nose. Encourage children to make similar statements.

PreK-Grade 1

The placement of the book itself involves spatial relationships: Where shall we put this book so that everyone can share it? Let's put it on the table or on top of the bookshelf.

Geometry & Spatial Sense

PreK–Grade 2

Point out the shape of the book and the objects in it, especially when they are unique. Whether the book is horizontal or vertical in design is also worth discussing. Within the book, illustrators sometimes frame the pages and, sometimes, various items or characters stick out of the frame. Encourage children to notice such spatial relationships.

Grades 1–2

Many of the shape books, such as Tana Hoban's, can be used as models for students to create their own books of shapes. Looking through a variety of shape books to make decisions about their own books encourages students to see the books in a new light.

K–Grade 2

Mapping activities are rich with spatial concepts. Create maps based on the journeys in books. Find maps of the geographical area of the book's setting. Use mapping to tell your own variation of a story.

Grades 1–2

Use the trips in some books (be it a trip to the store or across the country) to create maps. Often it is not clear precisely where various things are in relation to each other in the story. Looking for clues in the text and illustrations provides an opportunity to discuss spatial relationships. Encourage multiple interpretations of the locations.

Picture Books for Geometry & Spatial Sense

Allen, Pamela. *Who Sank the Boat?* Putnam, 1990. ISBN 0-698-20679-7
¿Quién hundió el bote? SRA, 1995. Available in Big Book and Small Book formats.
Good friends go for a row in the bay, but the boat sinks. (See page 2.)

Altman, Linda Jacobs. *Amelia's Road.* Illustrated by Enrique O. Sanchez. Lee & Low Books, 1993. ISBN 1-880000-04-0
Amelia hates roads and maps because her family travels to pick crops and, whenever her father takes out the map, she knows they will soon move on. (See page 3.)

Brett, Jan. *The Mitten: A Ukrainian Folktale.* Putnam, 1990. ISBN 0-399-21920-X
El mitón. SRA, 1995. Available in Big Book and Small Book formats. Audiocassette from Scholastic.
Larger and larger animals struggle to fit inside the mitten. (See page 7.)

Cole, Joanna. *The Magic School Bus Inside the Human Body.* Illustrated by Bruce Degen. Scholastic, 1989. ISBN 0-590-40759-7
El autobús mágico en el cuerpo humano. Spanish from Lectorum.
This book in the popular Magic School Bus series finds Ms. Frizzle taking her class on a field trip to the science museum to study the human body. Once again, the unexpected happens, and Ms. Frizzle ends up driving them into Arnold's body for a closeup view. The zany story is packed with information about the human body. The students fly into, around, and through various internal organs. (See page 15.)

Geometry & Spatial Sense

Derby, Sally. *The Mouse Who Owned the Sun.* Illustrated by Friso Henstra. Simon and Schuster, 1993. ISBN 0-02-766965-3
Mouse lives alone in the deep, dark woods. He's content with his existence mostly because he believes he owns the sun. He thinks so because he gets up early every morning and asks the sun to rise and it does. At night, when he is sleepy, he gets into bed and asks the sun to set and it follows his orders. In the end, he gives the sun to a king in exchange for a map. Mapping activities abound here. (See page 18.)

Dr. Seuss. *Yertle the Turtle and Other Stories.* Random, 1956. ISBN 0-394-80087-7
Audiocassette from David McKay.
In this typical Seuss fable, Yertle becomes master of all he surveys. He must be higher to be master of more. (See page 19.)

Hill, Elizabeth Starr. *Evan's Corner.* Illustrated by Sandra Speidel. Penguin USA, 1991. ISBN 0-670-82830-0
In the apartment where Evan lives with his family, there are only two rooms. Evan longs for a place of his own, and his mother figures out a way to divide two rooms equally among the eight members of the family. (See page 29.)

Hirst, Robin and Hirst, Sally. *My Place in Space.* Illustrated by Roland Harvey and Joe Levine. Orchard Books, 1990. ISBN 0-531-08459-0
Henry says his address is 12 Main Street, Gumbridge, Australia, Southern Hemisphere, Earth, solar system, solar neighborhood, Orion Arm, Milky Way Galaxy, local group of galaxies, Virgo Supercluster, the universe. There is material here for many levels of mapping activities. (See page 30.)

Hoban, Tana. *Circles, Triangles and Squares.* Simon and Schuster, 1974. ISBN 0-02-744830-4
Hoban's black-and-white photographs show us the shapes of familiar objects that we might previously have ignored: Bubbles, shoelace eyelets, and wheels on skates provide some of the circles. A passing crane and the spokes on a bicycle wheel give us some triangles, and we see squares in window screens and tennis rackets.

Hoban, Tana. *Look Again!* Simon and Schuster, 1971. ISBN 0-02-744050-8
We look through a small circle in an otherwise empty page and see a small part of a black-and-white photograph. We try to figure out what it is, turn the page, and affirm or deny our guesses by looking at the full object. Another turn of the page shows that object in a larger context.

Hoban, Tana. *Look! Look! Look!* Morrow, 1987. ISBN 0-688-07240-2
As in *Look Again*, the author/photographer shows us a small opening, sometimes a circle and other times a square, through which to view an object and then shows us larger and larger views of the object.

Hoban, Tana. *Look Up, Look Down.* Morrow, 1992. ISBN 0-688-10577-7
Color photographs highlight oil slicks, trash cans, and birds on telephone wires. The pattern is ABAB, and it is clear that the photographer is focusing on spatial relationships.

Hoban, Tana. *Over, Under and Through.* Simon and Schuster, 1973. ISBN 0-02-744820-7
A black-and-white exploration of spatial relationships.

Hoban, Tana. *Round and Round and Round.* Morrow, 1983. ISBN 0-688-01814-9
Now let's go on a photographic search for circles.

Hoban, Tana. *Shapes, Shapes, Shapes.* Morrow, 1986. ISBN 0-688-05833-7
This time the photographer combines black-and-white and color photographs to show us shapes such as circles, ovals, hexagons, parallelograms, and stars in common objects.

GEOMETRY & SPATIAL SENSE

Hoban, Tana. *Spirals, Curves, Fanshapes, and Lines.* Morrow, 1992. ISBN 0-688-11229-3
We see all the title shapes and more in these vivid color photographs, but we are also given puzzles to ponder: What are that clothesline and blanket doing in the drinking fountain?

Hoberman, Mary Ann. *A House Is a House for Me.* Illustrated by Betty Fraser. Penguin USA, 1978. ISBN 0-670-38016-4 Audiocassette from Live Oak.
A rhythmic text matches creatures with homes, starting out logically and getting a little zanier. This book leads us into a fixation with finding houses for things, which, of course, is all about spatial relationships. (See page 31.)

Hughes, Shirley. *Alfie Gets in First.* Morrow, 1982. ISBN 0-688-00849-6
We deal with characters inside and outside the house. (See page 32.)

Hutchins, Pat. *Rosie's Walk.* Simon and Schuster, 1968. ISBN 0-02-745850-4 Audiocassette from Weston Woods.
As Rosie, the hen, takes a barnyard stroll, we are given many position words that relate Rosie to her surroundings.

Kraus, Robert. *Where Are You Going, Little Mouse?* Morrow, 1986. ISBN 0-688-04295-3
Little Mouse is running away from home. He's off to find a mother, father, brother, and sister who will play with him and always be nice to him. The exuberant paintings follow him across water and through desert and jungle. There's *in* and *out* and *up* and *down* here as well as an opportunity for mapping. Children who are interested could map where he goes or map a journey of where they would go.

Lillegard, Dee. *Sitting in My Box.* Illustrated by Jon Agee. Penguin USA, 1989. ISBN 0-525-44528-5
A boy is just sitting in a cardboard box all by himself, and then, one by one, he is joined by a horde of creatures who all get in the box. (See page 38.)

Lillie, Patricia. *When This Box Is Full.* Illustrated by Donald Crews. Morrow, 1993. ISBN 0-688-12017-2
A child looks at an empty box and imagines the things she will put in it throughout the coming year. (See page 39.)

Lobel, Arnold. *Owl at Home.* HarperCollins, 1975. ISBN 0-06-023949-2 Audiocassette from HarperCollins.
In one story, Owl tries to be upstairs and downstairs at the same time.

Lobel, Arnold. *The Rose in My Garden.* Illustrated by Anita Lobel. Morrow, 1984. ISBN 0-688-02587-0
Another "This Is the House That Jack Built" story by Arnold and Anita Lobel tells of a simple incident in a garden. As each flower is mentioned, it is placed in relationship to the others: The bee sleeps on the rose, the marigolds stand by the hollyhocks, and the zinnias grow near the marigolds.

Martin, Bill Jr and Archambault, John. *Chicka Chicka Boom Boom.* Illustrated by Lois Ehlert. Simon & Schuster, 1989. ISBN 0-671-67949-X
Big Book, Small Book, and Audiocassette formats available from SRA.
A, B, and C climb up the coconut tree followed by all the other letters. When there's not enough room in the tree, the letters fall out of it. (See page 41.)

Mazer, Anne. *The Salamander Room.* Illustrated by Steve Johnson. Random, 1991. ISBN 0-394-92945-4
When a boy wants to keep his salamander in his room, his mother keeps asking questions, the answers to which involve changing the space considerably. (See page 42.)

Geometry & Spatial Sense

McMillan, Bruce. *Beach Ball—Left, Right.* Holiday House, 1992. ISBN 0-8234-0946-5
Full-color photographs show us a large beach ball somewhere on land or sea to help children learn about left and right. The side margin tells us *left* or *right.* Some suggestions are included for teaching the concept.

McMillan, Bruce. *Fire Engine Shapes.* Morrow, 1988. ISBN 0-688-07843-5
McMillan's full-color photographs use the fire engine as the container of many shapes: rectangles in the windows, triangles on the door hinges, and circles in the headlights, for instance.

Ringgold, Faith. *Tar Beach.* Random, 1991. ISBN 0-517-58031-4
The family, who lives in a city apartment, often goes up on the roof on summer evenings. While lying on a quilt on this tar beach, the girl imagines herself flying over the city. (See page 45.)

Measurement

Measurement includes the ability to measure, describe, and compare attributes of objects such as length, width, and weight. It includes the ability to compare the measurements of various objects and to recognize and convert various units of measure. Understanding measurement allows students to obtain and compare information about objects even when those objects are not physically present. It is used extensively in geometry and mapping and in data gathering.

Developmental Stages

At the PreK level, the children should have a clear understanding of attributes before beginning measurement concepts.

The understanding of the various attributes that can be measured, such as length, width, height, and weight, is developing at the kindergarten level. A beginning understanding of number allows children to begin to experiment with describing, for instance, how long something is. Nonstandard units, such as manipulative cubes, are most often used to determine and communicate measurement.

Their greater facility with numbers allows first-grade students to experiment more with measuring. Still using nonstandard units for the most part, students may begin to discover the need for standard units of measure.

Standard units are often formally introduced in second grade along with continuing experimentation with nonstandard units. Children gain greater facility in communicating about their measurements.

Using Picture Books for Measurement

Picture books can be springboards for many hands-on measurement projects in the classroom. Watch for books in which the size of something is important or in which various amounts are contrasted.

Measurement Activities

K–Grade 2

Most books can be used for measurement activities. What are the dimensions of this book? Will we need to put it on the shelves for oversized books or will it fit on the regular shelf?

PreK–Grade 2

Within the book, various sizes are often mentioned or shown. Which character is the biggest? Tallest? Smallest? Thinnest? Fattest? Which characters could come into your house? Your room? Your bed?

PreK–Grade 2

Many stories involve foods that you can cook in the classroom. While cooking, notice how measurement is used and the various units of measurement. Older students can be involved with the calculations to double and triple a recipe and with converting one unit to another. What fraction of a cup is eight tablespoons?

K–Grade 2

In stories where the characters are animals, look up the actual size of one or more of the animals involved. Make a template the size of the animal and use this template to take measurements. How many rabbits tall are you? How many tigers tall is our door? How many

MEASUREMENT

snakes long is our room? How many mice long is our table?

Grades 1–2

Again referring to the actual sizes of animals used as characters in the story, compare the information you have found to the book's illustrations. Did the illustrator choose to represent the animals at a realistic size relative to other objects in the illustrations? How big do you think the animals in the illustrations are? Are they larger or smaller than the real animals?

K–Grade 2

Cut pieces of string the actual size of an animal or some central object in the story. Can you find something in the classroom that is the same length?

Grades 1–2

When characters are outside, what might the temperature be? Do you think it is warmer or colder than the current temperature where you are? What clues are there? How could you test your guesses? Is it winter? What is the average daytime temperature in winter in your area? Does it look like it is colder or warmer in winter where the book is set?

Grades 1–2

As an extension of the previous activity, look for clues in your area about temperature. Looking out your classroom window, can you see anything that gives you a hint? Chart the daily temperature for a while and try to find clues that correspond to your recorded temperatures.

PICTURE BOOKS FOR MEASUREMENT

Allen, Pamela. *Who Sank the Boat?* Putnam, 1990. ISBN 0-698-20679-7
¿Quién hundió el bote? SRA, 1995. Available in Big Book and Small Book formats.
The relative size of the characters is a focal point of the book. (See page 2.)

Blundell, Tony. *Beware of Boys.* Morrow, 1992. ISBN 0-688-10925-X
A boy keeps a wolf so busy gathering and measuring ingredients for various ways to cook the boy that the wolf ends up exhausted and weak. (See page 6.)

Brett, Jan. *The Mitten: A Ukrainian Folktale.* Putnam, 1990. ISBN 0-399-21920-X
El mitón. SRA, 1995. Available in Big Book and Small Book formats.
Audiocassette from Scholastic. The size of the animals is important here. (See page 7.)

Bulloch, Ivan. *Measure.* Thomson, 1994. ISBN 1-56847-233-1
This is the second in the "Action Math" series. It uses color photographs and simple directions for activities involving measurement.

Carle, Eric. *The Grouchy Ladybug.* HarperCollins, 1977. ISBN 0-690-013292-2
La mariquita malhumorada. Spanish from Hispanic Book Distributors.
A grouchy ladybug challenges ever bigger animals to a fight.

Cole, Joanna. *The Magic School Bus Inside the Human Body.* Illustrated by Bruce Degen. Scholastic, 1989. ISBN 0-590-40759-7
El autobús mágico en el cuerpo humano. Spanish from Lectorum.
This book in the popular Magic School Bus series finds Ms. Frizzle taking her class on a field trip to

MEASUREMENT

the science museum to study the human body. Once again, the unexpected happens and Ms. Frizzle ends up driving them into Arnold's body for a closeup view. The zany story is packed with information about the human body, which is an area of study conducive to measurement activities. (See page 15.)

Dr. Seuss. *Yertle the Turtle and Other Stories*. Random, 1956. ISBN 0-394-80087-7 Audiocassette from David McKay.
Yertle measures his power by what he can see. (See page 19.)

Guiberson, Brenda. *Cactus Hotel*. Illustrated by Megan Lloyd. Henry Holt, 1991. ISBN 0-8050-1333-4
We examine the ecology of a desert by observing the life cycle of a giant cactus. As we follow its life from a seed to a mighty giant, we find references to its size and opportunities to find other things of similar size in our own environment. (See page 24.)

Henkes, Kevin. *Julius, the Baby of the World*. Morrow, 1990. ISBN 0-688-09700-6
Julius, el rey de la casa. Spanish from Lectorum. Child development, especially of babies, is full of measurement activities and is a central part of this book. (See page 28.)

Hirst, Robin and Hirst, Sally. *My Place in Space*. Illustrated by Roland Harvey and Joe Levine. Orchard Books, 1990. ISBN 0-531-08459-0
Henry gives his address as 12 Main Street, Gumbridge, Australia, Southern Hemisphere, Earth, solar system, solar neighborhood, Orion Arm, Milky Way Galaxy, local group of galaxies, Virgo Supercluster, the universe. The description of each locale introduces various units of measure. (See page 30.)

Hoban, Tana. *Is It Larger? Is It Smaller?* Morrow, 1985. ISBN 0-688-04028-4
In this book of photos, the questions are implied.

Johnston, Tony. *Farmer Mack Measures His Pig*. Illustrated by Megan Lloyd. HarperCollins, 1986. ISBN 0-06-023018-5
The book describes a competition between two pigs to find out which is fatter and the better jumper.

Koller, Jackie French. *Fish Fry Tonight*. Illustrated by Catharine O'Neill. Random, 1992. ISBN 0-517-57815-8
When Mouse catches a fish, she measures it against herself and declares it to be "as big as me." Unfortunately, she invites Squirrel to come for dinner along with a friend or two who each measure it against themselves. (See page 37.)

Lionni, Leo. *The Biggest House in the World*. Random, 1987. ISBN 0-394-82740-6
A snail wants the biggest house in the world, but it proves impractical.

Lionni, Leo. *Inch by Inch*. Astor-Honor, 1962. ISBN 0-8392-3010-9
The inchworm can measure almost anything, but the birds demand that he measure a nightingale's song.

Lobel, Arnold. *Frog and Toad Are Friends*. Harper, 1970. ISBN 0-06-023958-1 Audiocassette from HarperCollins.
Sapo y sepo son amigos. Spanish from Lectorum. Measurement of both time and distance are involved in these short stories. (See page 40.)

Martin, Bill Jr and Archambault, John. *Chicka Chicka Boom Boom*. Illustrated by Lois Ehlert. Simon & Schuster, 1989. ISBN 0-671-67949-X
Big Book, Small Book, and Audiocassette formats available from SRA.
A, B, and C climb up a coconut tree. Soon the rest of the letters follow, "Chicka chick boom boom! Will there be enough room?" Naturally it's not until the last letter, Z, climbs up, that the tree sways over, spilling them all in a heap. Can you set up a balance

scale to tip when you put the last letter in?
(See page 41.)

McMillan, Bruce. *Step by Step.* Morrow, 1987.
ISBN 0-688-07233-X
A boy goes from wiggler to walker in a series of
photographs.

McMillan, Bruce. *Time to . . .* Morrow, 1989.
ISBN 0-688-0856-2
The boy goes through his day measuring time by a
variety of clocks.

Van Laan, Nancy. *Rainbow Crow.* Illustrated by Beatriz
Vidal. Random, 1989. ISBN 0-394-89577-0
Danger comes for the animals when the snow
deepens. It is measured according to the size of
animals it buries. (See page 49.)

Wood, Audrey. *The Napping House.* Illustrated by Don
Wood. Harcourt, 1991. ISBN 0-15-256708-9
Audiocassette from Weston Woods.
This tale of an accumulating pile of nappers has
obvious size comparisons intrinsic to it.

Time

Time is one type of measurement. The understanding of time includes an understanding of the patterns that create days, weeks, months, and years. Working with time exposes the students to many units of measure and to a predictable repetition. Here we include activities and books about the passage of large and small amounts of time; the pattern of the seasons; and estimates of years, days, and hours.

Developmental Stages

In PreK, students are becoming aware that time can be broken into various parts. They begin to get a general sense of years, months, weeks, days, and hours, minutes, and seconds. In addition, they are developing a sense of when during the day routine things happen.

Kindergartners can begin to work with calendars and are becoming more familiar with the parts into which time is divided.

In order to understand the timekeeping of a clock, the students must have some understanding of numbers, proportion, and ordering. In first grade, students can work with the sequencing of events and correlating them with the calendar and the clock.

In second grade, students begin to measure time more accurately and, because of their developing understanding of measurement and fractions, they can compare and modify time measurements.

Using Picture Books for Time

The passage of time is frequently part of the story in a picture book. This passage of time can be estimated or altered to change the story.

Time Activities

PreK–Grade 1

Look for clues that indicate the time of day—morning, afternoon, or night.

PreK–Grade 2

In many books, the story takes place over a period of time. Sometimes that time is obvious, even stated, but in other books it's a bit more subtle. Children can be encouraged to estimate the amount of time that has passed between the first and last pages.

Grades 1–2

The copyright date can provide another opportunity to discuss time. When was this book first published? How long ago was that? How old were you or your parents when this book was published?

Grades 1–2

Figuring out which is the oldest book in your classroom library is another way of involving time.

Grades 1–2

Ask children to estimate how long it will take to read this book. Use a timer to check. Be careful, however, or this can lead to attempts to speed read most books, and that's definitely undesirable.

Time

Picture Books for Time

Adoff, Arnold. *Hard to Be Six*. Illustrated by Cheryl Hanna. Morrow, 1990. ISBN 0-688-09579-8
A six-year-old boy is counseled by his grandmother because he wants time to pass quickly.

Andrews, Jan. *The Very Last First Time*. Illustrated by Jan Wallace. Simon and Schuster, 1986. ISBN 0-689-50388-1
An Inuit girl fulfills her village's rite of passage by walking on the bottom of the sea under the ice when the tide is out. She loses track of time and barely makes it back.

Anno, Mitsumasa. *Anno's Sundial*. Putnam, 1987. ISBN 0-399-21374-0
This pop-up book explores the construction and use of sundials as well as the more basic concepts of the Earth's movement in space and its effect on the ways we calculate time.

Barrett, Judi. *Benjamin's 365 Birthdays*. Illustrated by Ron Barrett. Simon and Schuster, 1992. ISBN 0-689-3179-1
Benjamin loves getting presents so much that he wraps up his already opened birthday presents and unwraps one each day for a year.

Carle, Eric. *The Very Quiet Cricket*. Putnam, 1990. ISBN 0-399-21885-8
As other insects pass him, a very small cricket tries again and again to chirp by rubbing his wings together. The day passes and night comes before the cricket sees another cricket and is at last successful.

Carle, Eric. *The Grouchy Ladybug*. HarperCollins, 1977. ISBN 0-690-013292-2
La mariquita malhumorada. Spanish from Hispanic Book Distributors.
A grouchy ladybug challenges ever bigger animals to a fight while clocks on each page mark time.

Caseley, Judith. *Dear Annie*. Morrow, 1991. ISBN 0-688-1001- 2
Grandfather has been sending Annie postcards since the day she was born. At last she can answer them.

Cooney, Barbara. *Miss Rumphius*. Penguin USA, 1982. ISBN 0-670-47958-6
La Señorita Emilia. Spanish from Lectorum. Audiocassette from Kimbo.
We watch a person grow from childhood to old age and can search for clues to her age and to the period in which she is living. (See page 16.)

Emberley, Michael. *Welcome Back, Sun*. Little, 1993. ISBN 0-316-23647-0
In northern Norway, there have been six long months of darkness and a little girl longs to see the first sunrise.

Fox, Mem. *Time for Bed*. Illustrated by Jane Dyer. Harcourt, 1993. ISBN 0-15-288183-2
As nighttime comes, we watch the animals get ready to rest.

George, Jean. *Dear Rebecca, Winter Is Here*. Illustrated by Loretta Krupinski. HarperCollins, 1993. ISBN 0-06-021140-7
A grandmother ex-plains the winter solstice to her granddaughter.

Greenfield, Eloise. *Africa Dream*. Illustrated by Carole Byard. HarperCollins, 1989. ISBN 0-690-04776-2
A child fantasizes about the African home of her ancestors, where she imagines that her grandfather planted a seed that grew into ten mango trees for her.

Hirst, Robin and Hirst, Sally. *My Place in Space*. Illustrated by Roland Harvey and Joe Levine. Orchard Books, 1990. ISBN 0-531-08459-0
Henry gives his address as 12 Main Street, Gumbridge, Australia, Southern Hemisphere, Earth,

TIME

solar system, solar neighborhood, Orion Arm, Milky Way Galaxy, local group of galaxies, Virgo Supercluster, the universe. The description of each locale introduces various units of measure, including light years. There is also interesting material here for computing the time it would take to travel the various distances mentioned. (See page 30.)

Hutchins, Pat. *Clocks and More Clocks.* Simon and Schuster, 1994. ISBN 0-02-745921-7
Mr. Higgins buys a clock for his attic. To find out whether the clock is telling the right time, he buys another clock for his bedroom. He checks the time on one, but by the time he climbs the stairs to check the other clock a minute has passed and so the other clock shows a different time. Thinking one clock must be wrong he buys more clocks. Finally, the watchmaker shows him, with a watch, that all the clocks are the same. So Mr. Higgins buys the watch.

Lillie, Patricia. *When This Box Is Full.* Illustrated by Donald Crews. Morrow, 1993. ISBN 0-688-12017-2
Months and seasons of the year are the focus of the book. (See page 39.)

Lobel, Arnold. *Frog and Toad Are Friends.* Harper, 1970. ISBN 0-06-023958-1 Audiocassette from HarperCollins.
Sapo y sepo son amigos. Spanish from Lectorum. In one story here, Toad is determined to sleep until spring but refuses to acknowledge spring is here. (See page 40.)

McFarlane, Sheryl. *Waiting for the Whales.* Illustrated by Ron Lighburn. Putnam, 1993. ISBN 0-399-22515-3
A grandfather and his granddaughter wait each year for the whale migration.

McMillan, Bruce. *Step by Step.* Morrow, 1987. ISBN 0-688-07233-X
We watch a little boy moving around from the time

he is four months old until his is fourteen months old, and he goes from wiggler to walker in color photographs.

McMillan, Bruce. *Time to . . .* Morrow, 1989. ISBN 0-688—8856-2
The concept of telling time is developed through photographs. On each page is a photograph of a clock showing the hour on the left with a child going about his daily routine on the right. A second (digital) clock shows the time at the bottom of the page, introducing the concept of A.M. and P.M.

Sendak, Maurice. *Chicken Soup with Rice.* HarperCollins, 1962. ISBN 0-06-025535-8
Audiocassette from Weston Woods.
Sendak's ode to the seasons is in chantable form.

Sendak, Maurice. *Where the Wild Things Are.* HarperCollins, 1988. ISBN 0-06-025493-9
Donde viven los monstruos. Spanish from Lectorum. Audiocassette from Weston Woods. This classic tale involves time in two ways: the equation of time and distance when Max travels in his boat, and the time he is actually gone from home.

Shulevitz, Uri. *One Monday Morning.* Simon and Schuster, 1974. ISBN 0-684-13195-1
This is a delicate story of a lonely little boy and a chain of distinguished visitors. It also emphasizes the days of the week.

Spier, Peter. *Tin Lizzie.* Doubleday, 1987. ISBN 0-385-13342-1
The Model T Ford was first built in 1909, and we observe the way it and our society change in a fifty-year period.

Van Leeuwen, Jean. *Emma Bean.* Illustrated by Juan Wijngaard. Penguin USA, 1993. ISBN 0-8037-1393-2
Emma is a stuffed animal that watches Molly from birth to adolescence.

Time

Wells, Rosemary. *Waiting for the Evening Star*.
Illustrated by Susan Jeffers. Penguin USA, 1993.
ISBN 0-8037-1399-1
Time moves slowly on a farm in Vermont in the
1910s.

Wiesner, David. *Tuesday*. Houghton, 1991.
ISBN 0-395-55113-7
As the frogs go flying on their lily pads, we keep
track of the time of night to the precise minute.
(See page 51.)

Wood, Audrey. *The Napping House*. Illustrated by Don
Wood. Harcourt, 1991. ISBN 0-15-256708-9
Audiocassette from Weston Woods.
This tale builds a pile of sleeping creatures and
then puts a wakeful flea at the top. Less careful
observers may think that the action occurs during
one night. Others will notice that it's a rainy
afternoon.

Money

Although both money and time are measurement activities, we give each its own concept chapter to aid those who are looking for activities and books dealing directly with these types of measurement. Money, of course, includes coins and bills and computations with them.

Developmental Stages

In PreK and K, students are first introduced to various coins and dollar bills. Observing attributes and learning to recognize the different coins is appropriate at this stage. Because students are still developing their sense of conservation, it is too soon to do much manipulating with values.

In first grade, students can begin counting money and exchanging one type of coin for its equivalent value in another type of coin.

Second-grade students continue working with coins and bills, progressing to larger amounts of money and more complex manipulations with value.

Using Picture Books for Money

Some picture books provide opportunities for observing monetary transactions and for inspiring inquiries about money.

Money Activities

K–Grade 2

On many books, the price is listed. Note this with the children. Compare one book's price with those of others in the classroom. Why might this book have cost less or more than others?

Grades 1–2

In books where purchases are made, it's fun to estimate the cost of items when it is not stated.

Grades 1–2

Following the above activity, look in your community or in catalogs for the representative prices of the same purchase. How much money would the character need? Would there be tax? Can you find the same item(s) secondhand? How much money would you save?

Grade 2

Make estimates of the comparative wealth of various characters in a story. Children can state how they arrived at that estimate. Government figures can be used for cost of living estimates, the poverty line, per capita income, and so on. Sample household budgets can be devised at various income levels.

Grades 1–2

When working with base ten concepts, use pennies, dimes, and dollars as manipulatives. See Appendix A, Counting Books, (page 140) for names of books to use for place value and the numeration chapter (page 81) for more on place value.

Picture Books for Money

Adams, Barbara Johnston. *The Go-Around Dollar.* Illustrated by Joyce Zarins. Simon and Schuster, 1992. ISBN 0-02-700031-1
We watch a dollar bill as it is passed from person to person, ending up framed as the first dollar earned by the owners of a store.

Money

Brisson, Pat. *Benny's Pennies.* Illustrated by Bob Barner. Doubleday, 1993. ISBN 0-385-41602-4 Benny buys gifts for all of his family with his five pennies. (See page 9.)

Caple, Kathy. *The Purse.* Houghton, 1986. ISBN 0-395-41852-6 Katie faces several problems in this simple story. She identifies each problem and solves them one by one. Katie has some coins in a metal bandage box, and she loves the way they sound. Her sister tells her to carry a purse to be more grown up. To buy the purse, Katie has to spend the coins. Now she has a purse and no money, so she earns money by doing odd jobs. When she puts the money in the purse, it makes no sound so she puts the money in a bandage box.

DeFelice, Cynthia. *Mule Eggs.* Illustrated by Mike Shenon. Orchard, 1994. ISBN 00531-06843-9 When Patrick buys a farm, his farmer neighbors look down on his city ways. One neighbor sells him mule eggs so he can hatch his own mule.

Hill, Elizabeth Starr. *Evan's Corner.* Illustrated by Sandra Speidel. Penguin USA, 1991. ISBN 0-670-82830-0 In the apartment where Evan lives with his family, there are only two rooms. Evan longs for a place of his own and his mother gives him his own corner. Among the things he does to make the corner his own is purchase a pet turtle for 50 cents after earning the money one dime at a time carrying groceries. (See page 29.)

Hoban, Lillian. *Arthur's Funny Money.* HarperCollins, 1981. ISBN 0-06-022344-8 Audiocassette from HarperCollins. When Arthur and Violet go into the bike-washing business, Violet finds out how little Arthur knows about numbers and money.

Hoban, Tana. *Twenty-Six Letters and Ninety-Nine Cents.* Morrow, 1987. ISBN 0-688-06362-4 Photographs show us letters, which seem to be the plastic raised letters on magnets commonly used on refrigerators, and coins. The book is divided into two parts to show the letters and money separately. As a nice touch, an amount of money is shown in two or three combinations of coins.

Hutchins, Pat. *Don't Forget the Bacon!* Morrow, 1978. ISBN 0-688-06788-3 Audiocassette from Live Oak. A boy's mother sends him to the store for groceries. Chanting on the way, he incorporates into his chant everything he sees and buys all the wrong things.

Kimmel, Eric. *Four Dollars and Fifty Cents.* Holiday House, 1990. ISBN 0-8234-0817-5 Cowboy Shorty owes the Widow Macrae four dollars and fifty cents and will do almost anything to avoid paying it.

Maestro, Betsy and Maestro, Giulio. *Dollars and Cents for Harriet.* Random, 1988. ISBN 0-517-56958-2 Harriet, the elephant, wants to buy a gift for herself that costs five dollars. She finds ways to earn it in small increments, giving us a chance to see how coins in various combinations add up.

Schwartz, David M. *If You Made a Million.* Morrow, 1989. ISBN 0-688-07018-3 Starting with one dollar and proceeding to a million, this is a wonderful book involving much more than counting.

Viorst, Judith. *Alexander, Who Used to Be Rich Last Sunday.* Illustrated by Ray Cruz. Simon & Schuster, 1978. ISBN 0-689-30602-4 *Alexander, Que ere rico el dominogo pasado.* Simon & Schuster, 1989. ISBN 0-689-31590-2 Alexander starts with a dollar, feeling very rich. Slowly he spends it, a little at a time, until he no longer feels so rich. (See page 50.)

Money

Williams, Vera. *A Chair for My Mother*. Morrow, 1982.
ISBN 0-688-00915-8
After a fire burns all their belongings, a family saves
their change to buy a comfortable chair for the
mother to rest in after a hard day working as a
waitress.

Data Gathering & Analyzing

Gathering data is frequently a part of solving problems and satisfying curiosity. When we look up information to answer a question or to formulate new questions, we are gathering and analyzing data. When we conduct surveys and draw conclusions from them, we are gathering and analyzing data. This includes a lot of work with graphs and leads to mathematical tools like averaging and other computations.

Developmental Stages

At the PreK level, we begin gathering data and analyzing by identifying attributes, sorting, and classifying objects.

In kindergarten, students may be ready to begin recording the attributes they observe by using concrete graphing activities, such as picture graphs.

First grade students are often able to collect their own data by developing surveys and tabulating responses. They are continuing their work with picture graphs and manipulative graphs.

By second grade, students can usually formulate more complex surveys or research inquiries. They can use bar graphs to represent their findings and can discern more patterns and draw more conclusions from their data.

Using Picture Books for Data Gathering & Analyzing

Picture books can be sources of data when we collect information on the attributes of characters or other subjects in the book. In addition, picture books can lead us to questions ripe for a survey or to subjects suggesting research.

Data Gathering & Analyzing Activities

K–Grade 1

Choose a manipulative for each character in the story. You might choose one color for boys and one for girls, one color for children and one for adults, and so on. Setting each piece in a stack with others of the same color results in a manipulative graph of the different types of characters in the story.

Grades 1–2

You can graph almost anything within a story: numbers of various types of characters or degrees of excitement, fear, or danger within the action, for instance.

Grades 1–2

Because many books involve problem solving of one sort or another, you can analyze information within the book leading to the solution or lack of solution to the problem.

PreK–Grade 2

Many picture books inspire interest in new topics. Choose something of interest and find out more. As you gather information, look for ways that you can organize your information and compare it. Seize opportunities to tabulate findings, graph results, and otherwise manipulate the information you find.

K–Grade 2

Students might want to create questionnaires from ideas found in the story. They can survey each other, their families, or other classes in the school. Depending on their ages, they can work on creating

Data Gathering & Analyzing

questions so they can get the most useful data. Follow the survey with various graphs to show information and to draw conclusions based on the data.

K–Grade 2

If your classroom has a computer with access to the Internet, you can extend your survey to classes across the U.S. or Canada. You might even get lucky and find a class in a more distant country interested in your survey.

Picture Books for Data Gathering & Analyzing

Anno, Mitsumasa. *Anno's Flea Market.* Putnam, 1984. ISBN 0-399-21031-8
At this flea market, items are grouped by categories; however, it is sometimes a puzzle to figure out the sorting rule.

Eaylor, Byrd. *Everybody Needs a Rock.* Illustrated by Peter Parnall. Simon and Schuster, 1974. ISBN 0-684-13899-9
In beautiful prose the author enumerates ten rules for choosing your own personal rock. In so doing, she shows us many attributes of rocks.

Eaylor, Byrd. *Guess Who My Favorite Person Is.* Illustrated by Robert Andrew Parker. Simon and Schuster, 1992. ISBN 0-684-19514-3
The narrator joins a girl in her game called "tell-what-your-favorite-thing-is." Playing the game can become a data gathering and analyzing activity about everyone's favorite things. (See page 4.)

Blake, Jon. *Daley B.* Illustrated by Axel Scheffter. Candlewick Press, 1992. ISBN 1-56402-078-9
Daley B., who doesn't know he's a rabbit, collects data from the animals around him so he can decide where to live, what to eat, and what to do with his big feet. (See page 5.)

Brett, Jan. *Town Mouse, Country Mouse.* Putnam, 1994. ISBN 0-399-22622-2
There are a couple of twists in Brett's version of the well-known tale. This time it is mouse couples who exchange dwellings. (See page 8.)

Brown, Ruth. *The Picnic.* Dutton, 1993. ISBN 0-525-45012-2
A human family goes on a picnic, and we see the events from the point of view of the animals they unwittingly frighten and disturb. The family dog is the main threat to the animals. Take surveys on people's opinions about dogs. (See page 10.)

Browne, Eileen. *No Problem.* Illustrated by David Parkins. Candlewick, 1993. ISBN 1-56402-176-9
Mouse gets a disassembled kit from Rat. (See page 11.)

Carle, Eric. *The Grouchy Ladybug.* HarperCollins, 1977. ISBN 0-690-013292-2
La mariquita malhumorada. Spanish from Hispanic Book Distributors.
A grouchy ladybug challenges ever bigger animals to a fight.

Cole, Joanna. *The Magic School Bus Inside the Human Body.* Illustrated by Bruce Degen. Scholastic, 1989. ISBN 0-590-40759-7
El autobús mágico en el cuerpo humano. Spanish from Lectorum.
This book in the popular Magic School Bus series finds Ms. Frizzle taking her class on a field trip to the science museum to study the human body. Once again, the unexpected happens and Ms. Frizzle ends up driving them into Arnold's body for a

closeup view. The zany story is packed with information about the human body. We can use the information presented in the book to compile and compare information or as a stepping-off point to the collection of data from outside sources about body parts and functions. (See page 15.)

DeFelice, Cynthia. *Mule Eggs*. Illustrated by Mike Shenon. Orchard, 1994. ISBN 00531-06843-9
When Patrick, a city slicker, buys a farm, his neighbor decides to take advantage of his naiveté. It takes Patrick a while to discover the trick his neighbor has played on him, but he gets his revenge.

de Regniers, Beatrice Schenk. *So Many Cats!* Illustrated by Ellen Weiss. Houghton, 1985.
ISBN 0-89919-700-0
They started with one cat and then there were more. Each cat becomes part of the household and is described in full. (See page 17.)

Derby, Sally. *The Mouse Who Owned the Sun*. Illustrated by Friso Henstra. Simon and Schuster, 1993.
ISBN 0-02-766965-3
Mouse lives alone in the deep, dark woods. He's content with his existence because he believes he owns the sun. He thinks so because when he gets up early every morning and asks the sun to rise, it does. At night, when he is sleepy, he gets into bed and asks the sun to set, and it follows his orders. Here's a clear case of data analyzing gone awry. (See page 18.)

Dunrea, Olivier. *Eppie M. Says . . . .* Simon and Schuster, 1990. ISBN 0-02-733205-5
Ana B. dice . . . . SRA, 1995. Available in Big Book and Small Book formats from SRA.
Ben Salem tries each thing his sister Eppie M. says. Sometimes he proves her right, other times wrong, and still other times he decides he's not sure whether she's right or wrong. (See page 20.)

Fox, Mem. *Hattie and the Fox*. Illustrated by Patricia Mullins. Simon and Schuster, 1988.
ISBN 0-02-735470-9
As Hattie, a hen, sees something in the bushes, she identifies the "something" one part at a time until we all know what it is.

Gammell, Stephen. *Once Upon MacDonald's Farm*. Simon and Schuster, 1984. ISBN 0-02-737210-3
Erasé una vez, en la granja del señor MacDonald. SRA, 1995. Available in Big Book and Small Book formats.
MacDonald's farm had no animals. So he bought an elephant, a baboon, and a lion. Here's an opportunity to collect information about farm animals and their agricultural uses. (See page 23.)

Guiberson, Brenda. *Cactus Hotel*. Illustrated by Megan Lloyd. Henry Holt, 1991. ISBN 0-8050-1333-4
We examine the ecology of a desert by observing the life cycle of a giant cactus. The children can gather data about life cycles of various plants and animals. (See page 24.)

Heine, Helme. *The Most Wonderful Egg in the World*. Simon and Schuster, 1983. ISBN 0-689-50280-X
Three chickens vie to produce the world's most beautiful egg.

Heller, Ruth. *Chickens Aren't the Only Ones*. Putnam, 1981. ISBN 0-448-01872-1
Las gallinas no son las únicas. Spanish from Lectorum.
In this strikingly illustrated nonfiction book about egg layers, we see domestic birds, wild birds, insects, and dinosaurs. Collect data from the text or from reference books about the various animals. (See page 26.)

DATA GATHERING & ANALYZING

Henkes, Kevin. *Chester's Way.* Morrow, 1988.
ISBN 0-688-07608-4
Chester, un tipo con personalidad. SRA, 1995.
Available in Lap Book and Small Book formats.
Chester and Wilson have so many things in common that they can be hard to tell apart. They cut
their sandwiches the same way, they wear
matching Halloween costumes, and they always
carry a first aid kit, "just in case." (See page 27.)

Hill, Elizabeth Starr. *Evan's Corner.* Illustrated by
Sandra Speidel. Penguin USA, 1991.
ISBN 0-670-82830-0
In the apartment where Evan lives with his family,
there are only two rooms. Evan longs for a place
of his own, so his mother gives him his own corner to decorate and make his own. This is a fine
opportunity to investigate types of housing and
their availability. (See page 29.)

Hirst, Robin and Hirst, Sally. *My Place in Space.*
Illustrated by Roland Harvey and Joe Levine.
Orchard Books, 1990. ISBN 0-531-08459-0
Henry gives his address as 12 Main Street,
Gumbridge, Australia, Southern Hemisphere,
Earth, solar system, solar neighborhood, Orion
Arm, Milky Way Galaxy, local group of galaxies,
Virgo Supercluster, the universe. There are
numerous opportunities in the study of space to
collect and compare data about celestial objects.
(See page 30.)

Hoberman, Mary Ann. *A House Is a House for Me.*
Illustrated by Betty Fraser. Penguin USA, 1978.
ISBN 0-670-38016-4
Audiocassette from Live Oak. A rhythmic text
matches creatures with homes, starting out logi-
cally and then getting a little zanier.
(See page 31.)

Hughes, Shirley. *Alfie Gets in First.* Morrow, 1982.
ISBN 0-688-00849-6
Alfie, a boy of two or three, gets into the row

house and slams the door, leaving his mother and
baby sister outside without a key. (See page 32.)

Hurd, Edith Thacher. *Wilson's World.* Illustrated by
Clement Hurd. HarperCollins, 1994.
ISBN 0-06-443359-5
Wilson paints a beautiful globe. Step by step he
paints the evolution of life and civilization and ends
up with an overpopulated and polluted mess. He
starts over, but this time he paints people who take
care of the Earth.

Inkpen, Mick. *One Bear at Bedtime.* Little, 1988.
ISBN 0-316-41889-7
We count all the items on each page, but eventually
we search the pages for missing caterpillars.

Johnston, Tony. *Farmer Mack Measures His Pig.*
Illustrated by Megan Lloyd. HarperCollins, 1986.
ISBN 0-06-023018-5
The book describes a competition between two pigs
to find out which is fatter and the better jumper.

Johnston, Tony. *Yonder.* Illustrations by Lloyd Bloom.
Penguin USA, 1988. ISBN 0-8037-0278-7
This lyrical book tells of a farmer and his wife who
build a home and farm, plant a plum tree, and start
their family. We watch the seasons pass as the
family grows and prospers. (See page 34.)

Kalan, Robert. *Jump, Frog, Jump!* Illustrated by Byron
Barton. Morrow, 1981. ISBN 0-688-09241-1
¡Salta, ranita, salta! Spanish from Lectorum.
This cumulative tale starts with a fly and ends with
a frog nearly being caught by some boys. Each new
event becomes part of the pattern. (See page 36.)

Koller, Jackie French. *Fish Fry Tonight.* Illustrated by
Catharine O'Neill. Random, 1992.
ISBN 0-517-57815-8
When Mouse catches a fish, she declares it to be
as big as she. She invites Squirrel and tells him to
bring a friend or two for a fish fry. Unfortunately,

each animal declares the fish to be as big as it is. (See page 37.)

McMillan, Bruce. *Mouse Views: What the Class Pet Saw.* Holiday House, 1993. ISBN 0-8234-1008-0
The items in a classroom are seen from the perspective of a very small mouse.

McMillan, Bruce. *Step by Step.* Morrow, 1987. ISBN 0-688-07233-X
We watch a little boy moving around from the time he is four months old until he is fourteen months old, and he goes from wiggler to walker in color photographs. The pictures can be used to gather and analyze information on the stages of child development.

Pulver, Robin. *Mrs. Toggle's Zipper.* Illustrated by Robert W. Alley. Simon and Schuster, 1990. ISBN 0-02-775451-0
Mrs. Toggle, the teacher, got a new winter jacket for Christmas. She put it on and the zipper stuck. Not only that, but the thing-a-ma-jig that you use to open the zipper is missing. Everybody at school gets into the act of extricating Mrs. Toggle. (See page 44.)

Rylant, Cynthia. *The Relatives Came.* Illustrated by Stephen Gammell. Simon and Schuster, 1986. ISBN 0-02-777210-1
Vinieron los parients. SRA, 1995. Available in Big Book and Small Book formats.
This is an old-fashioned family reunion where the relatives come from far away and stay for days, giving us ample opportunity to view them and their antics. (See page 46.)

Stevenson, James. *The Mud Flat Olympics.* Morrow, 1994. ISBN 0-688-12823-4
The animals are having their own Olympics and, in four short chapters, plus a preface and epilogue, Stevenson presents their efforts in a mock serious tone. (See page 47.)

Van Allsburg, Chris. *The Garden of Abdul Gasazi.* Houghton, 1979. ISBN 0-395-27804-X
A dog, Fritz, and a boy enter the garden of a mysterious magician who might have turned Fritz into a duck. There is evidence to support both sides of that argument.

Van Leeuwen, Jean. *Emma Bean.* Illustrated by Juan Wijngaard. Penguin USA, 1993. ISBN 0-8037-1393-2
Emma is a stuffed animal that watches Molly from birth to adolescence.

Wiesner, David. *Tuesday.* Houghton, 1991. ISBN 0-395-55113-7
Frogs flying on lily pads invade the village during the night. Police and other investigators find no evidence, except lily pads all over the place. (See page 51.)

Young, Ed. *Seven Blind Mice.* Putnam, 1992. ISBN 0-399-22261-8
Each of seven blind mice sees one part of an elephant and, based on that limited information, identifies it incorrectly.

Zemach, Harve. *The Judge: An Untrue Tale.* Illustrated by Margot Zemach. Farrar, 1969. ISBN 0-374-33960-0
In this rhyming book, one after another witness is brought before the judge. Each witness adds another detail to the description of a monster who is heading their way.

Computation

According to *The Role of Routine Procedures in the Development of Mathematical Competence*, the 1990 Yearbook of the National Council of Teachers of Mathematics, "If we want students to remember procedures, we should ask them to step back and think about the procedures they are using rather than practicing more exercises."

It turns out that solid skills with computation come not so much from repeated drills of methods taught by a teacher, but from the students' ability to create their own methods of completing computations, and the deeper understanding provides the computation process itself. Flexibility and the ability to recognize more than one way of completing the task actually create a stronger math sense and, eventually, greater skill in manipulating numbers.

This type of computational ability develops when students are encouraged to work together to solve a problem, when a wide range of approaches to a calculation are solicited by the teacher, and when students are not penalized for doing things in unconventional ways. When the focus is on developing a method for solving a computation and on describing that process to others, students are forced to think more about what they did and why they did it than about whether they got the right answer. Students still want to get the right answer, of course, but they no longer cease thinking about the process when they discover whether their answer was right or wrong.

For more information on creating students with strong computation skills see Appendix B: Professional Resources (page 144) for books on the topic.

We are also including in this computation chapter work with estimation (which could have easily been placed in the numeration chapter) because it is intertwined with computation skills. The chapters on Measurement (page 91), Money (page 99), Data Gathering & Analyzing (page 102), and Fractions & Proportion (page 115) all list many books and activities that involve computation.

Developmental Stages

In PreK, the groundwork for computation ability includes free exploration of materials and development of communication skills about attributes and classification.

On the kindergarten level, groundwork for later computation ability includes developing a strong number sense. (See Numeration, page 81.) In particular, the ability to arrange a certain number of objects in various subgroups underlies computation. Kindergartners are able to see that groups can be composed of subgroups.

First-grade students begin combining and separating groups of objects for addition and subtraction. Addition and subtraction facts can be searched for patterns. Students learn to describe the process they used in adding and subtracting and to listen to the processes used by others.

At the second-grade level, adding and subtracting abilities extend to larger numbers and more complex methods of computing an answer. The focus is on flexibility of methods. Multiplication and division processes develop as students continue to manipulate numbers.

Using Picture Books for Computation

Some picture books contain obvious math computations, and these stories can be used as models for students to write their own math stories. When students write math stories or their own word problems, this writing serves multiple purposes. The students get to experiment with another kind of

COMPUTATION

writing and think through their ideas about numbers. Also, their writing often offers a window into their process so you can evaluate where they are in their work with numbers.

Other picture books introduce us to areas of interest where further exploration can involve computation as students attempt to answer their own questions about the subject.

COMPUTATION ACTIVITIES

Grades 1–2

Often a book with numerous characters can be used to estimate how many more would be needed to have ten, a hundred, or even a thousand in all.

Grades 1–2

Many books introduce particular foods that the class can prepare. The recipe you use provides a wealth of computation material. How large is a serving? How many servings do we need? Should the recipe be doubled? Tripled? Rewrite the recipe, substituting the new amounts.

Grade 2

Using a meal from the story, calculate it's nutritional value. Estimate serving size and look up the nutritional contents. Find the recommended daily allowance for a nutrient and determine how many servings the characters would have to eat to meet the requirement.

Grades 1–2

When you come across a number in a book, use computation to look for ways to better understand its value. If it's a weight, compute how many students it would take to equal that weight. If it's a distance, compute how long it would take a car to drive it or a person to walk it. Look for other ways to convert amounts to familiar quantities.

Grades 1–2

Subtraction is most commonly modeled as taking away. (There were ten cookies and Cindy ate three. How many cookies are left?) Look for instances in picture books of other models of subtraction, such as finding the difference between the number of boys and girls; determining subsets; and finding a missing amount.

Look at the activities in Data Gathering & Analyzing (page 102) and Measurement (page 91) to find more activities that naturally include computation.

PICTURE BOOKS FOR COMPUTATION

Anno, Mitsumasa. *Anno's Counting Book.* HarperCollins, 1977. ISBN 0-690-01288-8
Against a barren landscape, Anno presents sets of numbers and their numerals, the months and seasons, and even builds a village. There is so much to count and examine here that one look through is not enough.

Anno, Mitsumasa. *Anno's Math Games* I, II, and III. Putnam, 1991.
These are three separate picture books in which various functions of math are required in order to solve the puzzles or play the games. Many primary children will be confused or frustrated with these three math games books, but those who can follow the games should find them delightful. The puzzles increase in difficulty throughout each book.

COMPUTATION

Anno, Mitsumasa. *Anno's Mysterious Multiplying Jar.*
Putnam, 1983. ISBN 0-399-20951-4
Anno explores the factors of ten, but he does so in
a playful way that tends to delight and instruct
rather than frustrate the young reader.

Barry, David. *The Rajah's Rice.* Illustrated by Donna
Perrone. Freeman, 1994. ISBN 0-7167-6568-3
Subtitled "A Mathematical Folktale from India," this
book is just that. A young girl gets the Rajah to
promise her rice as calculated on a chess board,
doubling the previous amount on each square of
the board.

Brisson, Pat. *Benny's Pennies.* Illustrated by Bob
Barner. Doubleday, 1993. ISBN 0-385-41602-4
Benny has five new pennies, but he's got lots of
family members telling him what they want him to
buy with the money. When he returns from his
shopping trip, he discovers that he has satisfied
them all. Furthermore, his purchases make sense
and could conceivably be bought with the money.
(See page 9.)

Cleveland, David. *The April Rabbits.* Illustrated by Nurit
Karlin. Scholastic, 1986. ISBN 0-590-42369-X
Each day of April, David discovers that number of
rabbits in his life. This is a good counting book
because the story is funny and it combines ordinal
and cardinal numbers.

de Regniers, Beatrice Schenk. *So Many Cats!* Illustrated
by Ellen Weiss. Houghton, 1985.
ISBN 0-89919-700-0
They started with one lone and rather lonely cat
and then there were more. They come singly and in
groups. (See page 17.)

Fox, Mem. *Shoes from Grandpa.* Illustrated by Patricia
Mullins. Orchard, 1990. ISBN 0-531-08448-5
In this cumulative tale, each of Jessie's relatives
buys her clothing to go with the shoes her Grandpa
bought her. Illustrated with cut-paper collage, the
book is light and playful as Jessie's costume
becomes more and more elaborate. (See page 21.)

Giganti, Paul. *Each Orange Had 8 Slices: A Counting
Book.* Illustrated by Donald Crews. Morrow, 1992.
ISBN 0-688-10429-0
Children can count or multiply with this book of sets
and numbers.

Giganti, Paul. *How Many Snails?* Illustrated by Donald
Crews. Morrow, 1988. ISBN 0-688-06370-5
As we view different sites, we are asked to count a
variety of items. Then we count subsets.

Hill, Elizabeth Starr. *Evan's Corner.* Illustrated by Sandra
Speidel. Penguin USA, 1991. ISBN 0-670-82830-0
In the apartment where Evan lives with his family,
there are only two rooms for eight people. Evan
longs for a place of his own and is given a corner.
(See page 29.)

Hirst, Robin and Hirst, Sally. *My Place in Space.*
Illustrated by Roland Harvey and Joe Levine.
Orchard Books, 1990. ISBN 0-531-08459-0
Henry gives his address as 12 Main Street,
Gumbridge, Australia, Southern Hemisphere, Earth,
solar system, solar neighborhood, Orion Arm, Milky
Way Galaxy, local group of galaxies, Virgo
Supercluster, the universe. Computation can be
used to create scale models of the address as well
as to convert many of the measurements to famil-
iar forms of reference. (See page 30.)

Hoban, Tana. *Twenty-Six Letters and Ninety-Nine Cents.*
Morrow, 1987. ISBN 0-688-06362-4
Photographs show us letters, which seem to be the
plastic raised letters on magnets commonly used
on refrigerators, and coins. The book is divided into
two parts to show the letters and money separately. As a nice touch, an amount of money is shown in
two or three combinations of coins.

COMPUTATION

Hutchins, Pat. *The Doorbell Rang.* Morrow, 1986.
ISBN 0-688-05252-5
Llaman a la puerta. Spanish from Lectorum.
A brother and sister sit down to share a plate of
cookies. Every time the doorbell rings, however,
there are more friends to share the cookies with.
How many cookies will they each get now? How
many more friends can come before they run out of
cookies? (See page 33.)

Lillegard, Dee. *Sitting in My Box.* Illustrated by Jon Agee.
Penguin USA, 1989. ISBN 0-525-44528-5
A little boy is sitting in a big cardboard box when
someone knocks. It's a giraffe who is followed by an
elephant, a baboon, a lion, a hippopotamus, and a
flea. (See page 38.)

O'Keefe, Susan Heyboer. *One Hungry Monster: A
Counting Book in Rhyme.* Illustrated by Lynn
Munsinger. Little, 1989. ISBN 0-316-63385-2
Not only is this house infested with monsters, they
are rude, boisterous, and noisy monsters. More
importantly, they are hungry, and after they are
assembled, the boy gets food for them.

Pinczes, Elinor. *One Hundred Hungry Ants.* Houghton,
1993. ISBN 0-395-63116-5
One hundred ants are rushing off to a picnic.
Unfortunately, there's one ant who insists on
regrouping them.

Pulver, Robin. Mrs. Toggle's Zipper. Illustrated by Robert
W. Alley. Simon and Schuster, 1990.
ISBN 0-02-775451-0
Mrs. Toggle, the teacher, got a new winter jacket
for Christmas. She puts it on one cold winter morning and can't get it off because the zipper's stuck.
Not only that, but the thing-a-ma-jig that you use to
open the zipper is missing. Everybody at school gets
into the act of trying to extricate Mrs. Toggle, but
it's the custodian who finally does it (See page 44.)

Rylant, Cynthia. *The Relatives Came.* Illustrated by
Stephen Gammell. Simon and Schuster, 1986.
ISBN 0-02-777210-1
Vinieron los parients. SRA, 1995. Available in Big
Book and Small Book formats.
Here is a beautiful book about an old-fashioned fam-
ily reunion in which the relatives come from far
across the mountains and pile into and around the
house with love and exuberance. (See page 46.)

Schwartz, David M. *How Much Is a Million?* Illustrated
by Steven Kellogg. Morrow, 1985.
ISBN 0-688-04049-7
Not only a million, but a billion and a trillion are
shown in graphic ways that help children understand these difficult concepts.

Schwartz, David M. *If You Made a Million.* Morrow,
1989. ISBN 0-688-07018-3
Starting with one dollar and proceeding to a million,
this is a wonderful book involving much more than
counting.

Sloat, Teri. *From One to One Hundred.* Dutton, 1991.
ISBN 0-525-44764-4
In this book, we count sets. The pages are crowded
and, at times, confusing, but the target sets are
placed in isolation at the bottom of the page.

Stevenson, James. *The Mud Flat Olympics.* Morrow,
1994. ISBN 0-688-12823-4
The animals are having their own Olympic games
and, in four short chapters plus a preface and epilogue, Stevenson presents their efforts and results
in a mock serious tone Many of the math activities
in this delightful book are obvious and they should
be kep at the same level of enjoyment as the book
projects. (See page 47.)

COMPUTATION

Viorst, Judith. *Alexander, Who Used to Be Rich Last Sunday.* Illustrated by Ray Cruz. Simon and Schuster, 1978. ISBN 0-689-30602-4
Alexander, Que ere rico el dominogo pasado. Simon and Schuster, 1989. ISBN 0-689-31590-2
Alexander and his two older brothers get a dollar each from their grandparents on Sunday. Alexander falls victim to temptation and accidents, and we watch him as his money goes.
(See page 50.)

PERSPECTIVE

Exploring various ways of looking at a problem or at the world in general are important in the development of mathematical thinking. It helps us break the habit of thinking there is just one right way to do things and increases our flexibility when encountering something new.

USING PICTURE BOOKS FOR PERSPECTIVE

Many picture books do an excellent job of drawing us into the world from an unusual point of view—a picnic as viewed by the animals or a classroom as viewed by a mouse. With many of these books, reading them and casually sharing observations are enough to expose students to new perspectives. If the opportunity presents itself, here are some activity suggestions that will take you farther.

PERSPECTIVE ACTIVITIES

PreK-Grade 2

With some illustrations, physical perspective changes in the book. We are sometimes looking straight at the picture and on other pages our view is from above or the side. Note when the angle changes and what we see differently because of it.

PreK-Grade 2

Retell the story from another perspective. What would change? What would stay the same?

K-Grade 2

How many different perspectives can you think of for this story? Brainstorm a class list.

K-Grade 2

To get at a less physical kind of perspective in many books, you can ask questions such as "What does each character know? If they had more information, would they have done something differently? What does each character perceive about the others?"

PreK-Grade 2

Talk about perspective during discussions about problem solving. Many problems involve differing perceptions.

PICTURE BOOKS FOR PERSPECTIVE

Aardema, Verna. *Why Mosquitoes Buzz in People's Ears*. Illustrated by Leo and Diane Dillon. Penguin USA, 1975. ISBN 0-8037-6087-6   Audiocassette from Weston Woods.
This African tale uses the cumulative format. A mosquito says something foolish to the iguana, who puts sticks in his ears so that he will hear no more such foolishness. This causes a chain reaction. When the lion tries to straighten it out, he hears of the events from each perspective.

Anno, Mitsumasa. *Anno's Alphabet: An Adventure in Imagination*. HarperCollins, 1975. ISBN 0-690-00541-5
At first glance, this is a rather boring alphabet book. Look closer and you will see that the letters, apparently made of wood, are optical illusions, and there is something wrong with each picture. Hidden in the frames of the pages are objects whose names begin with that letter.

Brett, Jan. *Town Mouse, Country Mouse*. Putnam, 1994. ISBN 0-399-22622-2
Two mice couples exchange homes, so we see their landscapes from each others' points of view. (See page 8.)

Perspective

Erown, Ruth. *The Picnic*. Dutton, 1993.
ISBN 0-525-45012-2
We see a picnic of people from the woodland animals' point of view. (See page 10.)

Carle, Eric. *The Tiny Seed*. Picture Book Studio, 1991.
ISBN 0-88708-015-4
It's fall and the seeds are being blown along by the wind. One tiny seed survives to flower and scatter its seeds to the wind. Throughout the story we see the world from the perspective of the seed. (See page 13.)

Cole, Brock. *The Giant's Toe*. Farrar, 1986.
ISBN 0-374-32559-6
This is a sort of prequel to the story of Jack and the Beanstalk. (See page 14.)

Dorros, Arthur. *Abuela*. Illustrated by Elisa Kleven. Dutton, 1991. ISBN 0-525-44750-4 Available from SRA in Big Book and Small Book formats. Rosalba imagines flying with her abuela, her grandmother, over the city and seeing it from that perspective.

Fleming, Denise. *In the Tall, Tall Grass*. Henry Holt, 1991. ISBN 0-8050-1635-X
A toddler looks at the creatures in the grass from his point of view.

Hirst, Robin and Hirst, Sally. *My Place in Space*. Illustrated by Roland Harvey and Joe Levine. Orchard Books, 1990. ISBN 0-531-08459-0
Henry gives his address as 12 Main Street, Gumbridge, Australia, Southern Hemisphere, Earth, solar system, solar neighborhood, Orion Arm, Milky Way Galaxy, local group of galaxies, Virgo Supercluster, the universe. This book takes us, layer by layer, from the city bus to the universe, broadening our perspective as we go. (See page 30.)

Hoban, Tana. *Look Again!* Simon and Schuster, 1971.
ISBN 0-02-744050-8
We look through a small circle in an empty page and see part of a black-and-white photograph. We try to figure out what it is, turn the page, and check our ideas by looking at the full object. The next page shows that object in a larger context.

Hutchins, Pat. *Rosie's Walk*. Simon and Schuster, 1968. ISBN 0-02-745850-4
Audiocassette from Weston Woods.
Rosie, the hen, takes a leisurely walk around the barnyard, not heeding the fox, whom she foils at every turn.

Jonas, Ann. *Reflections*. Morrow, 1987.
ISBN 0-688-06141-9
We go through a day, looking at the illustrations first from front to back. Then we flip the book over and see the same illustrations upside down with different text, and they look quite different. (See page 35.)

Jonas, Ann. *Round Trip*. Morrow, 1983.
ISBN 0-688-01781-9
This is a black-and-white turnabout book.

London, Jonathan. *Voices of the Wild*. Illustrated by Wayne McLoughlin. Random, 1993.
ISBN 0-517-59218-5
A young man paddles his canoe through the wilderness, and we see him from the perspective of the animals along the way.

McMillan, Bruce. *Mouse Views: What the Class Pet Saw*. Holiday House, 1993. ISBN 0-8234-1008-0
The items in a classroom are seen from the perspective of a very small mouse.

Siebert, Diane. *Train Song*. Illustrated by Mike Wimmer. HarperCollins, 1990. ISBN 0-690-04728-2
The sights and sounds of trains are depicted in poetic prose and unusual perspectives. (See page 47.)

PERSPECTIVE

Van Allsburg, Chris. *Two Bad Ants.* Houghton, 1988.
ISBN 0-395-48668-8
After ants discover sugar crystals in a human's
kitchen, the queen asks for more. This time two
ants stay behind, and we see common kitchen
objects from an ant's perspective.

Wood, Audrey. *The Napping House.* Illustrated by Don
Wood. Harcourt, 1991. ISBN 0-15-256708-9
Audiocassette from Weston Woods.
The change in perspective is wonderful in this book.
We, the viewers, go from eye level to the ceiling and
back down again.

Young, Ed. *Seven Blind Mice.* Putnam, 1992.
ISBN 0-399-22261-8
Each of seven blind mice sees one part of an elephant and, based on that limited information, identifies it incorrectly.

Fractions & Proportion

Fractions and proportion are all tangled up with numeration and computation—especially division. Fractions are another kind of number and can be explored in the ways described in Numeration (see page 81). In addition, there is a lot of fraction and proportion work involved with Time (page 95) and Money (page 99).

Developmental Stages

PreK students should be exposed to the fractions in everyday activities. Terms such as *a half, a third,* and *a quarter* can be used. Asking children to divide continuous materials (such as clay) into two, three, or four equal amounts gives students concrete experience with fractions.

In kindergarten, this experience with everyday fractions continues.

At the first-grade level, students can divide noncontinuous materials in halves or quarters and other fractional amounts.

Second graders can begin to represent fractional amounts numerically and do some manipulating and comparing of fractions.

Using Picture Books for Fractions & Proportion

Some picture books play with fractions and proportions and can be used to extend children's exposure to fractions. Other picture books can be used for fraction and proportion activities that go beyond what is presented in the book.

Fractions & Proportion Activities

PreK–Grade 1

While sharing books with children, take opportunities to make such statements as "We're almost halfway through this book. Perhaps we can do the last half tomorrow" or "I think that the picture of the _____ is about a quarter of the way into the book."

PreK–Grade 2

While having small groups of children reorganize the classroom library, you can encourage them to make statements such as "We put half of the books on these shelves" or "We divided the books into four equal parts."

Grades 1–2

Use examples of division in a story to discuss fractions as well. Dividing twelve into four parts gives three each, or one fourth of twelve equals three.

Grades 1–2

Make diagrams (pie chart or equal sets) to illustrate the fractions from a picture book.

Grades 1–2

Students might want to write their own sharing stories (similar to *The Doorbell Rang*) to illustrate dividing something into fractions.

Fractions & Proportion

Picture Books for Fractions & Proportion

Blundell, Tony. *Beware of Boys*. Morrow, 1992.
ISBN 0-688-10925-X
When a boy is captured by a wolf, he uses his wits
to free himself—he keeps the wolf busy and
exhausted gathering ingredients for cooking boys.
(See page 6.)

de Regniers, Beatrice Schenk. *So Many Cats!* Illustrated
by Ellen Weiss. Houghton, 1985.
ISBN 0-89919-700-0
They started with one lone and rather lonely cat
and then there were more. As each cat becomes a
part of the household, the author re-counts them
and arrives at a new number. The repetitive text is
charming and the plot is one to which most cat
owners can relate. (See page 17.)

Giganti, Paul. *Each Orange Had 8 Slices: A Counting
Book*. Illustrated by Donald Crews. Morrow, 1992.
ISBN 0-688-10429-0
Children can count or multiply with this book of sets
and numbers.

Hill, Elizabeth Starr. *Evan's Corner*. Illustrated by Sandra
Speidel. Penguin USA, 1991. ISBN 0-670-82830-0
In the apartment where Evan lives with his family,
there are only two rooms for eight people. Evan
longs for a place of his own, so his mother gives
him his own corner to decorate and make his own.
How else could you divide the space into eighths?
(See page 29.)

Hutchins, Pat. *The Doorbell Rang*. Morrow, 1986.
ISBN 0-688-05252-5
Llaman a la puerta. Spanish from Lectorum.
A brother and sister sit down to share a plate of
cookies. Every time the doorbell rings, however,
there are more friends to share the cookies. The
children divide the cookies in halves, quarters,
sixths, and so on. (See page 33.)

Koller, Jackie French. *Fish Fry Tonight*. Illustrated by
Catharine O'Neill. Random, 1992.
ISBN 0-517-57815-8
When Mouse catches a fish, she gleefully invites
Squirrel and some of his friends to dinner that
evening, declaring that she has caught a fish as big
as she. Squirrel repeats the invitation to Rabbit,
declaring that Mouse has caught a fish as big as
he. The message and the increasing size of the fish
are repeated through the woods. (See page 37.)

McMillan, Bruce. *Eating Fractions*. Scholastic, 1991.
ISBN 0-590-43770-4
Clear color photographs show two children dividing
various foods into halves, thirds, and quarters, and
then having fun eating.

Pinczes, Elinor. *One Hundred Hungry Ants*. Houghton,
1993. ISBN 0-395-63116-5
One hundred ants are rushing off to a picnic.
Unfortunately, there's one ant who keeps regrouping them.

Section 4

Annotated Bibliography

ANNOTATED BIBLIOGRAPHY

The books that are predominantly counting books are listed in Appendix A, beginning on page 140.

Aardema, Verna. *Why Mosquitoes Buzz in People's Ears.* Illustrated by Leo and Diane Dillon. Penguin USA, 1975. ISBN 0-8037-6087-6 Available in Big Book format.
This African tale uses the cumulative format. A mosquito says something foolish to the iguana, who puts sticks in his ears so that he will hear no more such foolishness. This frightens the next animal who sees the iguana, and so goes the chain of action until a monkey inadvertently kills an owlet, which causes the mother owl to mourn and neglect her duty of waking the sun.
problem solving, time, patterns, perspective

Adams, Barbara Johnston. *The Go-Around Dollar.* Illustrated by Joyce Zarins. Simon and Schuster, 1992. ISBN 0-02-700031-1
We watch a dollar bill as it is passed from person to person, ending up framed as the first dollar earned by the owners of a store. At the same time, we get factual information about dollar bills, including an explanation for the symbols on our paper money.
money

Adoff, Arnold. *Hard to Be Six.* Illustrated by Cheryl Hanna. Morrow, 1990. ISBN 0-688-09579-8
A six-year-old boy is counseled by his grandmother because he wants time to pass quickly.
time

Ahlberg, Janet and Ahlberg, Allan. *The Baby's Catalogue.* Little, 1983. ISBN 0-316-02037-0
We look at items in the young child's world in a series of categories.
attributes & classification

Allen, Pamela. *Who Sank the Boat?* Putnam, 1990. ISBN 0-698-20679-7
¿Quién hundió el bote? SRA, 1995. Available in Big Book and Small Book formats.
A cow, a pig, a sheep, and a mouse decide to take a boat ride. They enter the boat from biggest to smallest, and each new passenger tips the boat and causes it to sit lower and lower in the water. The question is repeated and answered after each animal gets into the boat. Guess who gets in last. Guess who sinks the boat. [See page 2.]
measurement, estimation, data gathering & analyzing, attributes & classification, patterns, problem solving, geometry & spatial sense, numeration

Altman, Linda Jacobs. *Amelia's Road.* Illustrated by Enrique O. Sanchez. Lee & Low Books, 1993. ISBN 1-880000-04-0
Amelia hates roads and maps because her family travels to pick crops and, whenever her father takes out the map, she knows they will soon move on. This time she particularly hates to leave because she has found a teacher who has bothered to learn her name. [See page 3.]
attributes & classification, numeration, estimation, geometry & spatial sense

Andrews, Jan. *The Very Last First Time.* Illustrated by Jan Wallace. Simon and Schuster, 1986. ISBN 0-689-50388-1
An Inuit girl fulfills her village's rite of passage by walking on the bottom of the sea under the ice when the tide is out. She loses track of time and barely makes it back.
time

Anno, Mitsumasa. *Anno's Alphabet: An Adventure in Imagination.* HarperCollins, 1975. ISBN 0-690-00541-5
At first glance, this is a rather boring alphabet book. Look closer and you will see that the letters, apparently made of wood, are optical illusions, and there is something wrong with each picture. Further, hidden in the frames of the pages are objects whose names begin with that letter.
problem solving, perspective

ANNOTATED BIBLIOGRAPHY

Anno, Mitsumasa. *Anno's Counting Book.* HarperCollins, 1977. ISBN 0-690-01288-8 Available in Big Book format.

Against a barren landscape, Anno presents sets of numbers and their numerals, the months and seasons, and even builds us a village. There is so much to count and examine here that one look is not enough. In this book as in the other Anno books listed here, the author has included a page for adults working with children in mathematics.
numeration, computation, time

Anno, Mitsumasa. *Anno's Counting House.* Putnam, 1982. ISBN 0-399-20896-8

Through cut-out windows and exterior and interior views, we watch ten children move from a house on one side of the street to a house on the other. In so doing, we can count and see many combinations of ten.
numeration, computation

Anno, Mitsumasa. *Anno's Faces.* Putnam, 1989. ISBN 0-399-21711-8

Forty-seven fruits and vegetables appear on these pages, and we use an accompanying transparent strip to put smiling or frowning features on them.
patterns, numeration

Anno, Mitsumasa. *Anno's Flea Market.* Putnam, 1984. ISBN 0-399-21031-8

At this flea market, items are grouped by categories; however, it is sometimes a puzzle to figure out the rule.
attributes & classification, data gathering & analyzing

Anno, Mitsumasa. *Anno's Hat Tricks.* Putnam, 1985. ISBN 0-399-21212-4

This is a difficult puzzle for many primary children; however, some will be able to follow the binary logic quite well.
problem solving, probability

Anno, Mitsumasa. *Anno's Math Games* I, II, and III. Putnam, 1991.

As in the book above, many primary children will be confused or frustrated with these three math games books, but those who can follow it should find them delightful. The puzzles increase in difficulty throughout each book.
problem solving, computation, probability

Anno, Mitsumasa. *Anno's Mysterious Multiplying Jar.* Putnam, 1983. ISBN 0-399-20951-4

Here Anno explores the factors of ten, but he does so in a playful way that tends to delight and instruct rather than frustrate the young reader.
numeration, computation, problem solving, patterns

Anno, Mitsumasa. *Anno's Sundial.* Putnam, 1987. ISBN 0-399-21374-0

This pop-up book explores the construction and use of sundials as well as the more basic concepts of the Earth's movement in space and its effect on the ways we calculate time.
measurement, time

Anno, Mitsumasa. *Socrates and the Three Little Pigs.* Putnam, 1986. ISBN 0-399-21310-4

Here Anno explores probability. Most primary children won't be able to follow it beyond the first few steps, but even that is a wonderfully playful way to explore the concept.
probability

Anno, Mitsumasa. *Topsy-Turvies: Pictures to Stretch the Imagination.* Weatherhill, 1970. ISBN 0-8348-2004-8

Here is a world of impossibilities and optical illusions.
patterns, probability, problem solving

Anno, Mitsumasa. *Upside Downers.* Putnam, 1988. ISBN 0-399-21522-0

Space is manipulated and distorted in this book of visual puzzles.
geometry & spatial sense, problem solving

Annotated Bibliography

Barrett, Judi. *Benjamin's 365 Birthdays.* Illustrated by Ron Barrett. Simon and Schuster, 1992. ISBN 0-689-3179-1
Benjamin loves getting presents so much that he rewraps his opened birthday presents and unwraps one each day for a year.
time, numeration, problem solving

Barry, David. *The Rajah's Rice.* Illustrated by Donna Perrone. Freeman, 1994. ISBN 0-7167-6568-3
Subtitled "A Mathematical Folktale from India," this book is just that. A young girl gets the Rajah to promise her rice as calculated on a chess board, doubling the previous amount on each square of the board.
numeration, computation, problem solving, patterns, data gathering & analyzing

Baylor, Byrd. *Everybody Needs a Rock.* Illustrated by Peter Parnall. Simon and Schuster, 1974. ISBN 0-684-13899-9
In beautiful prose the author enumerates ten rules for choosing your own personal rock.
numeration, data gathering & analyzing, attributes & classification

Baylor, Byrd. *Guess Who My Favorite Person Is.* Illustrated by Robert Andrew Parker. Simon and Schuster, 1992. ISBN 0-684-19514-3
The narrator joins a girl in her game called "tell-what-your-favorite-thing-is." (See page 4.)
data gathering & analyzing, attributes & classification, patterns

Blake, Jon. *Daley B.* Illustrated by Axel Scheffter. Candlewick Press, 1992. ISBN 1-56402-078-9
Daley B. is an animal with a problem—he doesn't know where to live or what to eat and he doesn't know why his feet are so big. When a weasel tells Daley, "I eat rabbits! Rabbits like you!" Daley B. finds out that he is a rabbit, and he doesn't have to think to figure out how use his large feet to get rid of the weasel. (See page 5.)
data gathering & analyzing, attributes & classification, problem solving

Blundell, Tony. *Beware of Boys.* Morrow, 1992. ISBN 0-688-10925-X
When a boy is captured by a wolf, he uses his wits to free himself—he keeps the wolf busy and exhausted gathering ingredients for cooking boys. (See page 6.)
problem solving, attributes & classification, patterns, estimation, measurement, fractions & proportion, time

Brett, Jan. *The Mitten: A Ukrainian Folktale.* Putnam, 1990. ISBN 0-399-21920-X
El mitón. SRA, 1995. Available in Big Book and Small Book formats.
When a boy loses a white mitten in the snow, many animals decide it's perfect for their shelter. Bigger and bigger animals enter the mitten, each using their unique weapons. A mouse undoes the whole thing by making the bear sneeze. (See page 7.)
geometry & spatial sense, measurement, attributes & classification, numeration, time

Brett, Jan. *Town Mouse, Country Mouse.* Putnam, 1994. ISBN 0-399-22622-2
There are a couple of twists in Brett's intricately illustrated version of the familiar folktale. In this case, country and city mouse couples exchange houses. The ending shows us an owl and a house cat who are about to make the same deal. (See page 8.)
problem solving, attributes & classification, data gathering & analyzing, numeration, measurement, computation, patterns

Brisson, Pat. *Benny's Pennies.* Illustrated by Bob Barner. Doubleday, 1993. ISBN 0-385-41602-4
Benny has only five new pennies, and he's got lots of family members telling him what they want him to buy. When he returns from shopping, he has satisfied them all. Furthermore, his purchases make sense and could conceivably be bought with the money. (See page 9.)
computation, money, numeration

ANNOTATED BIBLIOGRAPHY

Brown, Margaret Wise. *Goodnight Moon.* Illustrated by Clement Hurd. HarperCollins, 1947.
ISBN 0-06-020706-X
Buenas noches luna. Available from Lectorum.
This classic has been around so long that we take it for granted, but the text that exactly fits the pictures makes it an ideal pattern book. The "goodnight" to everything in the room makes it a simple pattern, easily grasped and imitated.
patterns, time, numeration

Brown, Margaret Wise. *The Important Book.* Illustrated by Leonard Weisgard. HarperCollins, 1949.
ISBN 0-06-020721-3
The pattern for this list of attributes is the same throughout the book.
attributes & classification, patterns

Brown, Ruth. *A Dark Dark Tale.* Penguin USA, 1981.
ISBN 0-8037-0093-8 Available in Big Book format.
This is a funny, spooky tale about a dark, dark night and a dark, dark visitor to a dark, dark house. Read it aloud in your spookiest voice, but whisper or squeak the ending.
patterns, perspective, data gathering & analyzing

Brown, Ruth. *The Picnic.* Dutton, 1993.
ISBN 0-525-45012-2
A human family goes on a picnic, and we see the events from the point of view of the animals they unwittingly frighten and disturb. (See page 10.)
perspective, data gathering & analyzing, geometry & spatial sense

Browne, Eileen. *No Problem.* Illustrated by David Parkins. Candlewick, 1993. ISBN 1-56402-176-9
Mouse gets an unassembled kit from Rat. Without reading the instructions, Mouse assembles a contraption that she rides to Badger's house. Badger and Otter both attempt to remake the thing but with poor results. Shrew reads the directions, sorts the parts, and builds an airplane. (See page 11.)
problem solving, attributes & classification, data gathering & analyzing

Bulloch, Ivan. *Games.* Thomson, 1994.
ISBN 1-56847-231-5
This is one of a series of books called "Action Math." In this one, with simple directions and large colorful illustrations, the author gives us 30 math games that demonstrate and expand many sound math concepts.
numeration, patterns, probability, attributes & classification

Bulloch, Ivan. *Measure.* Thomson, 1994.
ISBN 1-56847-233-1
The second book in the "Action Math" series uses color photographs and simple directions to in a series of activities involving measurement.
measurement

Bulloch, Ivan. *Patterns.* Thomson, 1994.
ISBN 1-56847-230-7
This book is one of a series called "Action Math" and presents activities for young children investigating patterns.
patterns

Bulloch, Ivan. *Shapes.* Thomson, 1994.
ISBN 1-56847-232-3
The fourth and last in the series is an interesting exploration of shapes.
geometry & spatial sense

Butler, Stephen. *The Mouse and the Apple.* Morrow, 1994. ISBN 0-688-12811-4
A mouse sits under an apple tree and waits for its lone ripe apple to fall. One by one, other animals join the mouse until there are five animals waiting for the apple to drop. As each animal grows impatient, it tries in vain to make the apple fall and then leaves in disgust. When all are gone except the patient mouse, the apple falls and it's delicious.
(See page 12.)
attributes & classification, geometry & spatial sense, numeration, patterns

Annotated Bibliography

Caple, Kathy. *The Purse*. Houghton, 1986.
ISBN 0-395-41852-6
Katie faces several problems in this simple story. She identifies each problem and solves them one by one.
money, problem solving

Carle, Eric. *The Grouchy Ladybug*. HarperCollins, 1977.
ISBN 0-690-013292-2
La mariquita malhumorada. Available from Hispanic Book Distributors.
A grouchy ladybug challenges bigger animals to a fight. We keep track of the time as she does so.
time, measurement, data gathering & analyzing

Carle, Eric. *Rooster's Off to See the World*. Picture Book Studios, 1991. ISBN 0-88708-042-1
A rooster sets out on a journey and gathers companions on the way. In this tale, he loses them one by one as well.
patterns, numeration

Carle, Eric. *The Tiny Seed*. Picture Book Studio, 1991.
ISBN 0-88708-015-4
It's fall and the seeds are being blown along by the wind. One tiny seed survives to flower and scatter its seeds to the wind. (See page 13.)
attributes & classification, patterns, geometry & spatial sense, perspective

Carle, Eric. *The Very Busy Spider*. Putnam, 1989.
ISBN 0-399-21592-1
This delightfully simple book is as pleasant to touch as it is to view. The spider's web and the fly are raised from the page. This, combined with its repetitive text, should make it a favorite with the very young.
patterns, attributes & classification, time, measurement

Carle, Eric. *The Very Quiet Cricket*. Putnam, 1990.
ISBN 0-399-21885-8
As other insects pass him, making their unique sounds, a very small cricket tries again and again to chirp by rubbing his wings together. Each time a patterned sequence follows.
time, attributes & classification, patterns

Carlstrom, Nancy. *Jesse Bear, What Will You Wear?* Illustrated by Bruce Degen. Simon and Schuster, 1986. ISBN 0-02-717350-X
This favorite is a rhyming text of repeated questions and phrases and is full of exuberant silliness.
patterns, attributes & classification, time

Caseley, Judith. *Dear Annie*. Morrow, 1991.
ISBN 0-688-10011-2
Grandfather has been sending Annie postcards since the day she was born. At last she can answer them.
time

Cleveland, David. *The April Rabbits*. Illustrated by Nurit Karlin. Scholastic, 1986 ISBN 0-590-42369-X
Each day of April, David discovers that number of rabbits in his life. This is a good counting book because the story is funny and it combines ordinal and cardinal numbers.
numeration, computation, probability, estimation, time

Cole, Brock. *The Giant's Toe*. Farrar, 1986.
ISBN 0-374-32559-6
This is a sort of prequel to the story of Jack and the Beanstalk. A giant hacks off his toe, which becomes a small boy. The boy cooks the giant's hen that laid the golden eggs and throws away his harp. The giant is displeased, to say the least. (See page 14.)
measurement, estimation

ANNOTATED BIBLIOGRAPHY

Cole, Joanna. *The Magic School Bus Inside the Human Body.* Illustrated by Bruce Degen. Scholastic, 1989. ISBN 0-590-40759-7 Available in Big Book format *El autobús mágico en el cuerpo humano.* Available from Lectorum.

This book in the popular Magic School Bus series finds Ms. Frizzle taking her class on a field trip to the science museum to study the human body. Once again the unexpected happens, and Ms. Frizzle ends up driving them into Arnold's body for a close-up view. The zany story is packed with information about the human body. (See page 15.)
measurement, geometry & spatial sense, attributes & classification, patterns, data gathering & analyzing, numeration, computation.

Cooney, Barbara. *Miss Rumphius.* Penguin USA, 1982. ISBN 0-670-47958-6
La Señorita Emilia. Available from Lectorum.
Miss Rumphius tries to accomplish three things suggested by her grandfather when she was little: to travel widely, to live by the sea, and to leave the world more beautiful. The first two come with ease, but the third is harder. She accomplishes it by planting lupine everywhere she goes, leaving the countryside covered with beauty. (See page 16.)
attributes & classification, patterns, problem solving, estimation

Crews, Donald. *Bicycle Race.* Morrow, 1985. ISBN 0-688-05172-3
In this nearly wordless book, we watch twelve bicycle riders, each dressed in different colors with numbers clearly displayed, warm up, line up, and start off. Various riders take the lead and drop back. The book accents numerals and should encourage identification.
numeration

Crews, Donald. *Freight Train.* Morrow, 1978. ISBN 0-688-84165-1
With beautiful and deceptively simple illustrations and minimal text, we watch a freight train assembled, started, and running.
numeration, attributes & classification

Crews, Donald. *Ten Black Dots.* Morrow, 1986. ISBN 0-688-060678-4
Simple black dots in all sorts of environments become our counting device.
numeration, patterns

de Regniers, Beatrice Schenk. *So Many Cats!* Illustrated by Ellen Weiss. Houghton, 1985. ISBN 0-89919-700-0
They started with one lonely cat, and then there were more. They came singly and in groups, and each had its own name and personality. As each cat becomes a part of the household, the author recounts them and arrives at a new number. The repetitive text is charming and the plot is one to which most cat owners can relate. (See page 17.)
attributes & classification, computation, problem solving, data gathering & analyzing, patterns, fractions & proportion

Dee, Ruby. *Two Ways to Count to Ten.* Henry Holt, 1988. ISBN 0-8050-0407-6
In this retelling of an African folktale, the Leopard King has promised his daughter and his kingdom to anyone who can throw a spear so high it won't come down until after the count of ten. After many tries, the tiny antelope counts to ten by twos and wins the contest.
numeration, problem solving

DeFelice, Cynthia. *Mule Eggs.* Illustrated by Mike Shenon. Orchard, 1994. ISBN 0-531-06843-9
When Patrick, a city slicker, buys a farm, his farmer neighbors are scornful. One of them decides to play a trick on Patrick. Because Patrick is in the market for a mule, the farmer sells him "mule eggs" (in reality, pumpkins). Patrick falls for the trick for a while but then gets his revenge and even gets his money back.
money, problem solving, data gathering & analyzing, attributes & classification

ANNOTATED BIBLIOGRAPHY

Derby, Sally. *The Mouse Who Owned the Sun.* Illustrated by Friso Henstra. Simon and Schuster, 1993. ISBN 0-02-766965-3
Mouse lives alone in the deep, dark woods. He's content with his existence mostly because he believes he owns the sun. He thinks so because he gets up early every morning and asks the sun to rise and it does. At night, when he is sleepy, he gets into bed and asks the sun to set and it follows his orders. (See page 18.)
data gathering & analyzing, geometry & spatial sense, patterns, attributes & classification

Dorros, Arthur. *Abuela.* Illustrated by Elisa Kleven. Dutton, 1991. ISBN 0-525-44750-4
Available in Big Book and Small Book formats from SRA.
A little girl imagines flying with her grandmother, over the city and seeing it from that perspective.
perspective, geometry & spatial sense

Dr. Seuss. *Yertle the Turtle and Other Stories.* Random, 1956. ISBN 0-394-80087-7
This is typical Seuss—funny fables with zany pictures and rhymes. This one gives us not only Yertle, but also Gertrude McFuzz and some bragging animals as well. (See page 19.)
numeration, measurement, attributes & classification, geometry & spatial sense

Dunrea, Olivier. *Eppie M. Says . . . .* Simon and Schuster, 1990. ISBN 0-02-733205-5
Ana B. dice . . . . SRA, 1995. Available in Big Book and Small Book formats from SRA.
Eppie M. has filled Ben Salem with many "facts," such as walking backwards will get you to Australia and kissing a mama pig on the nose will turn you into a prince. Ben faithfully tests each of Eppie M.'s truisms. Sometimes he proves her wrong, sometimes right, and sometimes he concludes that he doesn't have enough information yet. The country setting and language, as well as the precise and comic illustrations, make this book a charmer. (See page 20.)
data gathering & analyzing

Emberley, Ed and Emberley, Barbara. *Drummer Hoff.* Simon and Schuster, 1985. ISBN 0-671-66682-7
Soldiers build a cannon and fire it off, whereupon it explodes. Rhythmic text and rhyme with striking woodcuts tell the story.
patterns, time, data gathering & analyzing

Emberley, Ed. *The Wing on a Flea: A Book about Shapes.* Little, 1988. ISBN 0-316-23600-4
This is a simple rhyming book about shapes.
geometry & spatial sense

Emberley, Michael. *Welcome Back, Sun.* Little, 1993. ISBN 0-316-23647-0
In northern Norway, there have been six long months of darkness, and a girl longs to see the first sunrise.
time

Everett, Percival. *The One That Got Away.* Illustrated by Dirk Zimmer. Houghton, 1992. ISBN 0-395-52550-3
Three cowboys rustle up a herd of ones. That's right, the numeral. The laughs are in the puns: "They caught one . . . . They went looking for another one." In the end, they return to where they had left eight ones to find "not a single one," but the numeral 8.
numeration

Fleming, Denise. *In the Tall, Tall Grass.* Henry Holt, 1991. ISBN 0-8050-1635-X
A toddler looks at the creatures in the grass from his point of view.
perspective

Fox, Mem. *Hattie and the Fox.* Illustrated by Patricia Mullins. Simon and Schuster, 1988. ISBN 0-02-735470-9
This is a little bit like "The Little Red Hen." Each animal has a suitably disdainful reply to the hen's observations—until the fox springs out. These remarks form the basis for the repetition.
patterns, data gathering & analyzing, probability, attributes & classification

Annotated Bibliography

Fox, Mem. *Shoes from Grandpa*. Illustrated by Patricia Mullins. Orchard, 1990. ISBN 0-531-08448-5
In this cumulative tale, each of Jessie's relatives buys her an article of clothing to go with the shoes her Grandpa bought her. Illustrated with cut-paper collage, the book is light and playful as Jessie's costume gets more and more elaborate. (See page 21.)
numeration, computation, money, patterns, attributes & classification, problem solving, geometry & spatial sense

Fox, Mem. *Time for Bed*. Illustrated by Jane Dyer. Harcourt, 1993. ISBN 0-15-288183-2
As night comes, we watch the animals get ready to rest.
time, patterns

Gackenbach, Dick. *King Wacky*. Random, 1984. ISBN 0-517-55265-5
King Wacky does everything backwards: he sits on a table and eats from a chair, he pays taxes to his people, and he says the opposite of what he means. Everything is fine until he tells the princess from another kingdom that she is the ugliest person he's ever seen. This book has attributes galore and inspiration to turn everything to its opposite.
perspective, attributes & classification, problem solving

Gaffney, Michael. *Secret Forests: A Collection of Hidden Creepy Crawly Bugs and Insects*. Artists and Writers, 1994. ISBN 0-307-17505-7
This oversized informational book shows the creatures within one habitat in isolation on a page together with a brief text about that creature. The following page shows the creature camouflaged in its habitat. The book provides opportunities for browsing, casual learning, and finding specific information. (See page 22.)
patterns, attributes & classification, geometry & spatial sense

Gammell, Stephen. *Once Upon MacDonald's Farm*. Simon and Schuster, 1984. ISBN 0-02-737210-3
Erasé una vez, en la granja del señor MacDonald. SRA, 1995. Available in Big Book and Small Book formats.
MacDonald had no animals. So he bought an elephant, a baboon, and a lion. His neighbor came to the rescue and gave him a horse, a cow, and a chicken. All seemed well until MacDonald started his chores—using the chicken to pull the plow. (See page 23.)
patterns, problem solving, data gathering & analyzing, numeration, attributes & classification

George, Jean. *Dear Rebecca, Winter Is Here*. Illustrated by Loretta Krupinski. HarperCollins, 1993. ISBN 0-06-021140-7
A grandmother explains the winter solstice to her young granddaughter.
time

Giganti, Paul. *Each Orange Had 8 Slices: A Counting Book*. Illustrated by Donald Crews. Morrow, 1992. ISBN 0-688-10429-0
Children can count or multiply with this book of sets and numbers.
fractions & proportion, numeration, computation

Giganti, Paul. *How Many Snails?* Illustrated by Donald Crews. Morrow, 1988. ISBN 0-688-06370-5
As we view different sites, we count a variety of items. Then we count subsets.
numeration, computation, patterns

Ginsburg, Mirra. *Across the Stream*. Illustrated by Nancy Tafuri. Morrow, 1982. ISBN 0-688-01206-X
Available in Big Book format.
A hen and three chicks are disturbed by a fox. To escape, they cross a stream on the backs of a duck and three ducklings.
numeration, problem solving

ANNOTATED BIBLIOGRAPHY

Gollub, Matthew. *The Twenty-Five Mixtec Cats.* Illustrated by Leovigildo Martinez. Morrow, 1993. ISBN 0-688-11640-X
The inhabitants of Oaxaca, Mexico, are not pleased with the number of cats in their healer's house.
numeration

Greenfield, Eloise. *Africa Dream.* Illustrated by Carole Byard. HarperCollins, 1989. ISBN 0-690-04776-2
A child fantasizes about the African home of her ancestors, where she imagines that her grandfather planted a seed that grew into ten mango trees for her.
numeration, time

Guiberson, Brenda. *Cactus Hotel.* Illustrated by Megan Lloyd. Henry Holt, 1991. ISBN 0-8050-1333-4
We examine the ecology of a desert through the life cycle of a giant cactus. (See page 24.)
patterns, attributes & classification, time, data gathering & analyzing, numeration

Hadithi, Mwenye. *Hungry Hyena.* Illustrated by Adrienne Kennaway. Little, 1994. ISBN 0-316-33715-3
Hungry Hyena has tricked Fish Eagle out of his meal of fish for the last time. Fish Eagle and Pangolin plan a trick, which has Hungry Hyena and all the other hyenas climbing atop each other to try for "the sweetest meat in all the world." The hyenas become, from then on, slower runners.
(See page 25.)
attributes & classification, patterns, estimation, computation, problem solving

Heine, Helme. *The Most Wonderful Egg in the World.* Simon and Schuster, 1983. ISBN 0-689-50280-X
Three chickens vie to produce the world's most beautiful egg.
attributes & classification, data gathering & analyzing

Heller, Ruth. *Chickens Aren't the Only Ones.* Putnam, 1981. ISBN 0-448-01872-1
Las gallinas no son las únicas. Available from Lectorum.
This strikingly illustrated nonfiction book is about egg layers. With rhythmic text and vibrant paintings, we see domestic birds, wild birds, insects, and dinosaurs. Every egg layer Heller could find is here. (See page 26.)
attributes & classification, patterns, data gathering & analyzing

Hendry, Diana. *Christmas on Exeter Street.* Illustrated by John Lawrence. Random, 1989. ISBN 0-679-90134-5
The house is elegant and a perfect place for a picture-book Christmas. Then the relatives and the neighbors, invited and not invited, show up, and somehow they find room for all the houseguests.
numeration, estimation, probability

Henkes, Kevin. *Chester's Way.* Morrow, 1988. ISBN 0-688-07608-4
Chester, un tipo con personalidad. SRA, 1995. Available in Lap Book and Small Book formats. Chester and Wilson are alike in so many ways, it's no wonder that they're the best of friends. Then Lilly moves into the neighborhood. She is unconventional, somewhat rowdy, and a bit of a daredevil. (See page 27.)
numeration, attributes & classification, patterns, problem solving, data gathering & analyzing

Henkes, Kevin. *Julius, the Baby of the World.* Morrow, 1990. ISBN 0-688-09700-6
Julius, el rey de la casa. Available from Lectorum.
Everyone loves the new baby except Lilly, his big sister. She does everything she can to make his life miserable until her cousin starts saying mean things about him. Then Lilly's hackles are raised to defend him, and she discovers to her surprise that he is soft, sweet, and lovable. (See page 28.)
attributes & classification, patterns, measurement, geometry & spatial sense, numeration, estimation

ANNOTATED BIBLIOGRAPHY

Heuck, Sigrid. *Who Stole the Apples?* Random, 1986. ISBN 0-394-82623-X
A rebus format is used in a repetitive text.
problem solving

Hill, Elizabeth Starr. *Evan's Corner.* Illustrated by Sandra Speidel. Penguin USA, 1991. ISBN 0-670-82830-0
In the apartment where Evan lives with his family, there are only two rooms. Evan longs for a place of his own and is given a corner. He furnishes it only to find that something's missing—company. (See page 29.)
problem solving, geometry & spatial sense, computation, money, data gathering & analyzing, attributes & classification

Hirst, Robin and Hirst, Sally. *My Place in Space.* Illustrated by Roland Harvey and Joe Levine. Orchard Books, 1990. ISBN 0-531-08459-0
Henry and Rosie tell the city bus driver that they want him to take them home. When he teases them that maybe they don't know the address of where they live, Henry rises to the occasion and tells the driver precisely where he lives: 12 Main Street, Gumbridge, Australia, Southern Hemisphere, Earth, solar system, solar neighborhood, Orion Arm, Milky Way Galaxy, local group of galaxies, Virgo Supercluster, the universe. During Henry's description, we also get a brief description of each part of the address. The result is a clear picture of our "place in space"and a glimpse at the amazing distances involved. (See page 30.)
measurement, time, data gathering & analyzing, numeration, geometry & spatial sense, computation, attributes & classification

Hoban, Lillian. *Arthur's Funny Money.* HarperCollins, 1981. ISBN 0-06-022344-8 When Arthur and Violet go into the bike-washing businees, Violet finds out how little Arthur knows about numbers and money.
money

Hoban, Tana. *Circles, Triangles and Squares.* Simon and Schuster, 1974. ISBN 0-02-744830-4
Hoban's black-and-white photographs show us the shapes of familiar objects that we might previously have ignored—circles in bubbles, shoelace eyelets, and wheels on skates; triangles on a passing crane and the spokes on a bicycle wheel; squares in window screens and tennis rackets.
geometry & spatial sense, patterns, attributes & classification

Hoban, Tana. *Colors Everywhere.* Morrow, 1995. ISBN 0-688-12762-2
In this wordless concept book, Hoban presents a variety of colored photographs of objects and animals on each page. At the side of the page is a Mondrian-like panel showing the colors that can be found on that page. It's one of Hoban's most successful and striking books.
patterns, attributes & classification

Hoban, Tana. *Count and See.* Simon and Schuster, 1972. ISBN 0-02-744800-2
Hoban gives us interesting objects to count in her black-and-white photographs.
numeration, patterns

Hoban, Tana. *Dots, Spots, Speckles, and Stripes.* Morrow, 1987. ISBN 0-688-06862-6
Vivid photographs wordlessly illustrate patterns in feathers, flowers, people, and animals.
patterns, attributes & classification

Hoban, Tana. *Exactly the Opposite.* Morrow, 1990. ISBN 0-688-08862-7
As in other opposite books, the ABAB pattern is clear. From Hoban's typically vivid photographs, we learn vocabulary as well as pattern.
patterns, attributes & classification

ANNOTATED BIBLIOGRAPHY

Hoban, Tana. *Is It Larger? Is It Smaller?* Morrow, 1985. ISBN 0-688-04028-4
In this book of photos, the questions are implied, not stated.
attributes & classification, measurement

Hoban, Tana. *Is It Red? Is It Yellow? Is It Blue?* Morrow, 1978. ISBN 0-688-84171-6
As the title implies, color is the system for classifying. The question is asked wordlessly by the colored circles at the bottom of the pages.
patterns, attributes & classification

Hoban, Tana. *Is It Rough? Is It Smooth? Is It Shiny?* Morrow, 1984. ISBN 0-688-03824-7
Texture is the classification system in this book with full-color photographs that seem to invite us to touch.
patterns, attributes & classification

Hoban, Tana. *Look Again!* Simon and Schuster, 1971. ISBN 0-02-744050-8
We look through a small circle in an otherwise empty page and see a small part of a black-and-white photograph. We try to figure out what it is, turn the page, and assess our ideas by looking at the full object. Another turn of the page shows that object in a larger context.
patterns, estimation, attributes & classification, perspective

Hoban, Tana. *Look! Look! Look!* Morrow, 1987. ISBN 0-688-07240-2
As in *Look Again*, the author/photographer shows us a small opening, sometimes a circle and other times a square, through which to view an object and then shows us larger and larger views of the object.
patterns, estimation, attributes & classification, perspective

Hoban, Tana. *Look Up, Look Down.* Morrow, 1992. ISBN 0-688-10577-7
Color photographs highlight oil slicks, trash cans, and birds on telephone wires. The pattern is ABAB and the photographer's focus is clearly spatial relationships.
geometry & spatial sense

Hoban, Tana. *Over, Under and Through.* Simon and Schuster, 1973. ISBN 0-02-744820-7
A black-and-white exploration of spatial relationships.
geometry & spatial sense

Hoban, Tana. *Round and Round and Round.* Morrow, 1983. ISBN 0-688-01814-9
A photographic search for circles.
geometry & spatial sense

Hoban, Tana. *Shapes, Shapes, Shapes.* Morrow, 1986. ISBN 0-688-05833-7
This time the photographer combines black-and-white and color photographs to show us shapes such as circles, ovals, hexagons, parallelograms, and stars in common objects.
geometry & spatial sense, patterns

Hoban, Tana. *Spirals, Curves, Fanshapes, and Lines.* Morrow, 1992. ISBN 0-688-11229-3
We see all the title shapes and more in these vivid color photographs, but we are also given puzzles to ponder: What are that clothesline and blanket doing in the drinking fountain?
geometry & spatial sense, patterns

Hoban, Tana. *Twenty-Six Letters and Ninety-Nine Cents.* Morrow, 1987. ISBN 0-688-06362-4
Photographs show us letters, which seem to be the plastic raised letters on magnets commonly used on refrigerators, and coins. The book is divided into two parts to show the letters and money separately. As a nice touch, an amount of money is shown in two or three combinations of coins.
numeration, computation, money, attributes & classification

ANNOTATED BIBLIOGRAPHY

Hoberman, Mary Ann. *A House Is a House for Me.* Illustrated by Betty Fraser. Penguin USA, 1978. ISBN 0-670-38016-4
A rhythmic text matches creatures with homes, starting out logically and getting a little zanier. (See page 31.)
attributes & classification, data gathering & analyzing, numeration, patterns

Hopkinson, Deborah. *Sweet Clara and the Freedom Quilt.* Illustrated by James Ransome. Random, 1993. ISBN 0-679-82311-5
A young slave stitches a quilt with a map pattern that will lead her to freedom.
patterns, geometry & spatial sense

Hort, Lenny. *How Many Stars in the Sky?* Illustrated by James Ransome. Morrow, 1991. ISBN 0-688-10104-6
A father and child attempt to count the stars.
numeration, patterns

Hughes, Shirley. *Alfie Gets in First.* Morrow, 1982. ISBN 0-688-00849-6
Alfie, a boy of two or three, gets into the row house and slams the door, leaving his mother and baby sister outside without a key. Neighbors gather, but Alfie solves the problem himself. (See page 32.)
problem solving, numeration, data gathering & analyzing, attributes & classification, geometry & spatial sense

Hurd, Edith Thatcher. *Wilson's World.* Illustrated by Clement Hurd. HarperTrophy, 1994. ISBN 0-06-443359-5
Wilson paints a beautiful globe. Step by step he paints the evolution of life and civilization. He ends up with an overpopulated and polluted mess. To solve his problem he starts over, only this time he paints people who take care of the Earth.
problem solving, data gathering & analyzing

Hutchins, Pat. *Clocks and More Clocks.* Simon and Schuster,1994. ISBN 0-02-745921-7
Mr. Higgins buys a clock for his attic. To find out whether the clock is telling the right time, he buys another clock for his bedroom. He checks the time on one, but by the time he climbs the stairs to check the other clock a minute has passed, and so the other clock shows a different time. Thinking one clock must be wrong, he buys more clocks. Finally, the watchmaker shows him, with a watch, that all the clocks are the same. So Mr. Higgins buys the watch.
time, problem solving

Hutchins, Pat. *Don't Forget the Bacon!* Morrow, 1978. ISBN 0-688-06788-3
A boy's mother sends him to the store for "Six farm eggs,/a cake for tea,/a pound of pears,/and don't forget the bacon." Chanting as he goes, it becomes "Six clothes pegs,/a rake for leaves,/and a pile of chairs," but he forgets the bacon. Following his chant or making your own changing shopping list are pattern activities.
patterns, money

Hutchins, Pat. *The Doorbell Rang.* Morrow, 1986. ISBN 0-688-05252-5
Llaman a la puerta. Available from Lectorum.
The story doesn't tell us how many cookies there are at the beginning, but it does tell us how many there are for each child as more and more children arrive. "No one makes cookies like Grandma's" is part of the predictable pattern. (See page 33.)
patterns, computation, estimation

Hutchins, Pat. *Rosie's Walk.* Simon and Schuster, 1968. ISBN 0-02-745850-4 Available in Big Book format from Scholastic.
Rosie, the hen, takes a leisurely walk around the barnyard, not heeding the fox, whom she foils at every turn. The words are easily decipherable because they are all prepositional phrases that detail Rosie's walk while completely ignoring the fox, who is never mentioned in the text. The illustrations are full of unusual patterns, and predicting what will

happen next to the fox brings students into the plot's pattern.

patterns, geometry & spatial sense, probability, perspective

Inkpen, Mick. *One Bear at Bedtime.* Little, 1988. ISBN 0-316-41889-7
We count all the items on each page, but eventually we search the pages for missing caterpillars.

numeration, patterns, data gathering & analyzing

Johnson, Paul Brett. *The Cow Who Wouldn't Come Down.* Orchard, 1993. ISBN 0-531-08631-3
The problem here is the cow up there, defying all logic and gravity.

problem solving

Johnston, Tony. *Farmer Mack Measures His Pig.* Illustrated by Megan Lloyd. HarperCollins, 1986. ISBN 0-06-023018-5
The book describes a competition between two pigs to find out which is fatter and the better jumper.

measurement, attributes & classification, data gathering & analyzing

Johnston, Tony. *Yonder.* Illustrations by Lloyd Bloom. Penguin USA, 1988. ISBN 0-8037-0278-7
This lyrical and beautiful book tells of a farmer and his wife who build a home and farm, plant a plum tree, and start their family. We watch the seasons pass and the family and tree grow until one becomes many. (See page 34.)

time, data gathering & analyzing, estimation, patterns, geometry & spatial sense

Jonas, Ann. *Reflections.* Morrow, 1987. ISBN 0-688-06141-9
There's a twist to this day in the life of a child by the sea, exploring ocean, pond, and woods. When you get to the end of the book, you flip it upside down and continue from the back page to the front. The boats on the sea at dawn, turned upside down, become birds and a plane in the sunset sky. This time everything looks different. (See page 35.)

perspective, attributes & classification, patterns, geometry & spatial sense

Jonas, Ann. *Round Trip.* Morrow, 1983. ISBN 0-688-01781-9
This is a black-and-white turnabout book.

perspective, patterns

Kalan, Robert. *Jump, Frog, Jump!* Illustrated by Byron Barton. Morrow, 1981. ISBN 0-688-09241-1
Available in Big Book format from Scholastic. *¡Salta, ranita, salta!* Available from Lectorum.
A cumulative tale that starts with a fly and ends with a frog nearly being caught by some boys. Each new event becomes part of the repeated pattern. (See page 36.)

patterns, data gathering & analyzing, geometry & spatial sense

Kimmel, Eric. *Four Dollars and Fifty Cents.* Holiday House, 1990. ISBN 0-8234-0817-5
Cowboy Shorty owes the Widow Macrae four dollars and fifty cents and will do almost anything to avoid paying it.

money

Kitchen, Bert. *Animal Numbers.* Penguin USA, 1987. ISBN 0-8037-0459-3
Fifteen animals are shown with their offspring, and readers are asked to determine how many are in each brood.

numeration, attributes & classification

Koller, Jackie French. *Fish Fry Tonight.* Illustrated by Catharine O'Neill. Random, 1992. ISBN 0-517-57815-8
Mouse catches a fish, the biggest one she ever caught, and she is ecstatic. She gleefully invites Squirrel and some of his friends to dinner that evening, declaring that she has caught a fish as big as she. Squirrel repeats the invitation to Rabbit, declaring that Mouse has caught a fish as big as

he. The message and the increasing size are repeated through the woods. When Mouse opens her door to let her dinner companions in, she is aghast at their number and size. However, Mouse is resourceful, to say the least, and a good hostess. (See page 37.)
measurement, data gathering & analyzing, problem solving, attributes & classification, fractions & proportion

Koscielniak, Bruce. *Bear and Bunny Grow Tomatoes*. Random, 1993. ISBN 0-679-93687-4
Bear and Bunny both start gardens. Bear is careful to do everything right—preparing the soil and tending the plants. Bunny throws the seeds on the ground and then sits back to watch. Bunny's antics as he waits for his tomatoes are silly and make this book wonderful in spite of the standard plot. The sequencing in the book is pronounced.
numeration, problem solving

Kraus, Robert. *Where Are You Going, Little Mouse?* Morrow, 1986. ISBN 0-688-04295-3
Little Mouse is running away from home. He's off to find a mother, father, brother, and sister who will play with him and always be nice to him. The exuberant paintings follow him across water and through desert and jungle in his search. There's *in* and *out* and *up* and *down* here as well as an opportunity for mapping.
geometry & spatial sense, problem solving

Lillegard, Dee. *Sitting in My Box*. Illustrated by Jon Agee. Penguin USA, 1989. ISBN 0-525-44528-5
Available in Big Book format.
A little boy is sitting in a big cardboard box when someone knocks. It's a giraffe who is followed by an elephant, a baboon, a lion, a hippopotamus, and a flea. The text is rhythmic with a strong pattern. (See page 38.)
patterns, geometry & spatial sense, numeration, computation

Lillie, Patricia. *When This Box Is Full*. Illustrated by Donald Crews. Morrow, 1993. ISBN 0-688-12017-2
Each month the young girl puts new items in the box. (See page 39.)
geometry & spatial sense, attributes & classification, numeration, time

Lionni, Leo. *The Biggest House in the World*. Random, 1987. ISBN 0-394-82740-6
A snail wants the biggest house in the world, but it proves impractical.
measurement

Lionni, Leo. *Inch by Inch*. Astor-Honor, 1962. ISBN 0-8392-3010-9
An inchworm can measure almost anything, but the birds demand that he measure a nightingale's song.
measurement

Lobel, Arnold. *Frog and Toad Are Friends*. HarperCollins, 1970. ISBN 0-06-023958-1
Sapo y sepo son amigos. Available from Lectorum. This simple book has been around a long time. It contains five short stories about Frog and Toad, who are good friends despite their different personalities. (See page 40.)
attributes & classification, numeration, time, measurement

Lobel, Arnold. *Owl at Home*. HarperCollins, 1975. ISBN 0-06-023949-2
This easy-to-read book has several stories. One concerns Owl's efforts to be upstairs and downstairs at the same time.
time, measurement, attributes & classification

Lobel, Arnold. *The Rose in My Garden*. Illustrated by Anita Lobel. Morrow, 1984. ISBN 0-688-02587-0
The "This Is the House That Jack Built" format is a simple incident in a garden. The words will stretch the mind, and the illustrations will delight the eye.
patterns, geometry & spatial sense

Annotated Bibliography

London, Jonathan. *Voices of the Wild.* Illustrated by Wayne McLoughlin. Random, 1993. ISBN 0-517-59218-5
A young man paddles his canoe through the wilderness, and we see him from the perspective of the animals along the way.
perspective

Maestro, Betsy and Maestro, Giulio. *Dollars and Cents for Harriet.* Random, 1988. ISBN 0-517-56958-2
Harriet, the elephant, wants to buy a gift for herself that costs five dollars. She finds ways to earn it in small increments, giving us a chance to see how coins in various combinations add up to the desired amount.
money

Martin, Bill Jr and Archambault, John. *Chicka Chicka Boom Boom.* Illustrated by Lois Ehlert. Simon & Schuster, 1989. ISBN 0-671-67949-X
Big Book, Small Book, and Audiocassette formats available from SRA.
A, B, and C climb up a coconut tree. Soon the rest of the letters follow. "Chicka chick boom boom! Will there be enough room?" Naturally, it's not until the last letter, Z, climbs up that the tree sways over, spilling them all in a heap. (See page 41.)
numeration, attributes & classification, measurement, geometry & spatial sense, patterns

Mazer, Anne. *The Salamander Room.* Illustrated by Steve Johnson. Random, 1991. ISBN 0-394-92945-4
A boy wants to keep the salamander he found in the woods. His mother keeps asking questions: Where will he sleep? What will he eat? Each time, the boy responds with an answer that makes sense as far as the salamander is concerned, but which will mean turning his room into a forest. (See page 42.)
problem solving, patterns, geometry & spatial sense, measurement

McFarlane, Sheryl. *Waiting for the Whales.* Illustrated by Ron Lighburn. Putnam, 1993. ISBN 0-399-22515-3
A grandfather and his granddaughter wait each year for the whale migration.
time, patterns

McMillan, Bruce. *Beach Ball—Left, Right.* Holiday House, 1992. ISBN 0-8234-0946-5
Full-color photographs show us a large beach ball somewhere on land or sea, and the side margin tells us *left* or *right.* Some suggestions are included for teaching the concept.
patterns, geometry & spatial sense

McMillan, Bruce. *Becca Backward, Becca Frontward: A Book of Concept Pairs.* Morrow, 1986. ISBN 0-688-06283-0
The ABAB pattern is clear in this book of colored photographs in which a dozen pairs of opposites are pointed out in the actions and reactions of a little girl.
attributes & classification, patterns

McMillan, Bruce. *Counting Wildflowers.* Morrow, 1986. ISBN 0-688-02860-8
These are beautiful photographs in which we are supposed to count the wildflower blossoms. We can also concentrate on numerous properties.
numeration, attributes & classification

McMillan, Bruce. *Dry or Wet.* Morrow, 1988. ISBN 0-688-07100-7
Concepts are presented on facing pages as seen through the antics of children.
attributes & classification

McMillan, Bruce. *Eating Fractions.* Scholastic, 1991. ISBN 0-590-43770-4
Available in Big Book format.
Clear color photographs show two children dividing various foods into halves, thirds, and quarters, and then having fun eating.
fractions and proportion, patterns

Annotated Bibliography

McMillan, Bruce. *Fire Engine Shapes*. Morrow, 1988.
ISBN 0-688-07843-5
McMillan's photographs use the fire engine as the container of many shapes: rectangles in the windows, triangles on the door hinges, and circles in the headlights.
patterns, geometry & spatial sense

McMillan, Bruce. *Mouse Views: What the Class Pet Saw*. Holiday House, 1993. ISBN 0-8234-1008-0
The items in a classroom are seen from the perspective of a very small mouse.
perspective, data gathering & analyzing

McMillan, Bruce. *One Two One Pair*. Scholastic, 1991.
ISBN 0-590-43767-4
First, we see the separate elements, and then two of them make a pair. There are opportunities here for left and right spatial relationships, patterning, and numeration.
geometry & spatial sense, patterns, numeration

McMillan, Bruce. *Step by Step*. Morrow, 1987.
ISBN 0-688-07233-X
We watch a little boy moving around from the time he is four months old until he's fourteen months old, and he goes from wiggler to walker in color photographs.
time, measurement, numeration

McMillan, Bruce. *Time to . . . .* Morrow, 1989.
ISBN 0-688-8856-2
The concept of telling time is developed through photographs. On each page is a photograph of a clock showing the hour on the left with a child going about his daily routine on the right. A digital clock shows the time at the bottom of the page, introducing the concept of A.M. and P.M.
time, measurement

Morris, Ann. *Hats, Hats, Hats*. Morrow, 1989.
Photographs by Ken Heyman. ISBN 0-688-06339-X
Colored photographs from around the world show us not only hats to examine and categorize but also interactions among the people wearing those hats.
attributes & classification

Neitzel, Shirley. *The Jacket I Wear in the Snow*.
Illustrated by Nancy Winslow Parker. Morrow, 1989. ISBN 0-688-08030-8
Available in Big Book format from Scholastic. Using a "This Is the House That Jack Built" pattern, every piece of clothing is placed on a boy who can then do everything but walk. (See page 43.)
patterns, attributes & classification, problem solving

Numeroff, Laura Joffe. *If You Give a Mouse a Cookie*.
Illustrated by Felicia Bond. HarperCollins, 1985.
ISBN 0-06-024587-5 Available in Big Book format from Scholastic.
Each action causes another until we're back to the beginning cookie and mouse.
patterns, problem solving

O'Keefe, Susan Heyboer. *One Hungry Monster: A Counting Book in Rhyme*. Illustrated by Lynn Munsinger. Little, 1989. ISBN 0-316-63385-2
Not only is this house infested with monsters, but they are rude, boisterous, and noisy monsters. More importantly, they are hungry and after they are assembled, one by one, the boy gets food for them.
numeration, computation, problem solving

Parnall, Peter. *Feet!* Simon and Schuster, 1988.
ISBN 0-02-770110-7
We take a close look at the feet of various animals, and the illustrations with the text give us things to sort and words to describe the feet.
attributes & classification

ANNOTATED BIBLIOGRAPHY

Pinczes, Elinor. *One Hundred Hungry Ants*. Houghton, 1993. ISBN 0-395-63116-5
One hundred ants are rushing off to a picnic, but there's one ant who keeps regrouping them.
problem solving, numeration, computation

Podwal, Mark. *The Book of Tens*. Morrow, 1994. ISBN 0-688-12994-3
This book examines the number ten as it occurs in the Old Testament. Each citing of ten is accompanied by a short paragraph explaining the allusion.
numeration, patterns

Pulver, Robin. *Mrs. Toggle's Zipper*. Illustrated by Robert W. Alley. Simon and Schuster, 1990. ISBN 0-02-775451-0
Mrs. Toggle, the teacher, gets a new winter jacket for Christmas. She puts it on one cold winter morning, and she can't get it off because the zipper's stuck. Not only that, but the thing-a-ma-jig that you use to open the zipper is missing. Everybody at school gets into the act of trying to extricate Mrs. Toggle, but it's the custodian who finally does it. (See page 44.)
numeration, computation, problem solving, data gathering & analyzing, attributes & classification

Reiss, John J. *Numbers*. Simon and Schuster, 1982. ISBN 0-02-776150-9
Reiss takes us all the way to 1000 in this beautiful counting book of simple shapes and vibrant colors.
geometry & spatial sense, numeration, patterns, attributes & classification

Ringgold, Faith. *Tar Beach*. Random, 1991. ISBN 0-517-58031-4
This book was inspired by a quilt made by the author. It's about a family who lives in a city apartment and often goes up on the roof on hot summer evenings. They call their roof "tar beach." While lying on a quilt on tar beach, the girl imagines herself flying over the city, and anything she flies over she owns. (See page 45.)
patterns, geometry & spatial sense

Rylant, Cynthia. *The Relatives Came*. Illustrated by Stephen Gammell. Simon and Schuster, 1986. ISBN 0-02-777210-1
Vinieron los parients. SRA, 1995. Available in Big Book and Small Book formats.
This is an old-fashioned family reunion where the relatives come from far across the mountains and pile into and around the house with love and exuberance. (See page 46.)
attributes & classification, numeration, computation, data gathering & analyzing, time, estimation, patterns

Schwartz, David M. *How Much Is a Million?* Illustrated by Steven Kellog. Morrow, 1985. ISBN 0-688-04049-7
Not only a million, but a billion and a trillion are shown in graphic ways that help children understand these difficult concepts.
numeration, computation

Schwartz, David M. *If You Made a Million*. Morrow, 1989. ISBN 0-688-07018-3
Starting with one dollar and proceeding to a million, this is a wonderful book involving more than counting.
numeration, money

Sendak, Maurice. *Chicken Soup with Rice*. HarperCollins, 1962. ISBN 0-06-025535-8
Available in Big Book format from Scholastic.
Sendak's ode to the seasons far precedes the current interest in pattern books, but it certainly fits the criteria.
time, patterns

Sendak, Maurice. *Where the Wild Things Are*. HarperCollins, 1988. ISBN 0-06-025493-9
Donde viven los monstruos. Available from Lectorum.
This classic tale involves time in two ways: the equation of time and distance when Max travels in his boat, and the time he is actually gone from home.
time

Shulevitz, Uri. *One Monday Morning.* Simon and Schuster, 1974. ISBN 0-684-13195-1
This is a delicate story of a lonely little boy and a chain of distinguished visitors. It also emphasizes the days of the week.
time, patterns, numeration

Siebert, Diane. *Train Song.* Illustrated by Mike Wimmer. HarperCollins, 1990. ISBN 0-690-04728-2
The sights and sounds of trains are depicted in poetic prose and unusual perspectives.
(See page 47.)
numeration, attributes & classification, patterns

Sis, Peter. *Going Up! A Color Counting Book.* Morrow, 1989. ISBN 0-688-08126-6
An elevator goes up through an apartment building, and on each floor Mary is joined by a neighbor. But such neighbors! There are many costumes and, of course, there are colors. We count neighbors, colors, and floors. There are cardinal numbers as well.
numeration, patterns, attributes & classification

Sloat, Teri. *From One to One Hundred.* Dutton, 1991. ISBN 0-525-44764-4
In this book, we count sets. The pages are crowded and, at times, confusing, but the target sets are placed in isolation at the bottom of the page. We go from one to ten and, by tens, to one hundred.
numeration, computation

Spier, Peter. *Crash! Bang! Boom!* Doubleday, 1990. ISBN 0-385-26569-7
As Spier fills his pages with sound makers, we get a chance to sort and classify the sources of all that noise.
attributes & classification

Spier, Peter. *Fast-Slow High-Low: A Book of Opposites.* Doubleday, 1972. ISBN 0-385-06781-X
Spier fills each page with careful and detailed watercolors of pairs of opposites.
attributes & classification, numeration

Spier, Peter. *Gobble, Grunt, Growl.* Doubleday, 1971. ISBN 0-385-24094-5
As in *Crash! Bang! Boom!,* Spier classifies noise-makers.
attributes & classification

Spier, Peter. *People.* Doubleday, 1980. ISBN 0-385-24469-X
In oversized pages jam-packed full of people and their qualities and aspects, Spier shows us many ways in which we are alike and different. There are a few regrettable stereotypes here, but the overall book is worth it.
attributes & classification

Spier, Peter. *Peter Spier's Rain.* Doubleday, 1987. ISBN 0-385-15485-2
In this wordless book, we watch two children experience a summer rain. After showing us many vignettes of the children and animals in the rain, Spier takes us indoors to show us rainy-day activities in that venue.
attributes & classification, geometry & spatial sense

Spier, Peter. *Tin Lizzie.* Doubleday, 1987. ISBN 0-385-13342-1
The Model-T Ford was first built in 1909, and we observe the way it and our society change in a fifty-year period.
time

Stevenson, James. *The Mud Flat Olympics.* Morrow, 1994. ISBN 0-688-12823-4
The animals are having their own Olympics and, in four short chapters, plus a preface and epilogue, Stevenson presents their efforts in a mock serious tone. We begin with the carrying of the torch by

ANNOTATED BIBLIOGRAPHY

Burbank. Then the contests begin. We have the Deepest Hole Digging, the All-Snail High Hurdles, the Smelliest Skunk Contest, and the Cross River Freestyle. (See page 47.)
data gathering & analyzing, estimation, attributes & classification, computation, patterns, problem solving, numeration

Van Allsburg, Chris. *The Garden of Abdul Gasazi.* Houghton, 1979. ISBN 0-395-27804-X
A dog, Fritz, and a boy enter the garden of a mysterious magician who may or may not have turned Fritz into a duck. There is evidence to support both sides of that argument.
problem solving, data gathering & analyzing

Van Allsburg, Chris. *Two Bad Ants.* Houghton, 1988. ISBN 0-395-48668-8
After ants discover sugar crystals in a human's kitchen, the queen asks for more. This time two ants stay behind, and we see common kitchen objects from an ant's perspective.
perspective

Van Laan, Nancy. *Rainbow Crow.* Illustrated by Beatriz Vidal. Random, 1989. ISBN 0-394-89577-0
This is a Lenape Indian legend that tells why the crow is black and has a hoarse voice. When heavy snow fell on earth and threatened to bury even the largest of animals, they asked the beautiful rainbow crow, who at that time had a glorious voice, to fly to the Great Sky Spirit for help. (See page 49.)
geometry & spatial sense, measurement, patterns, time, attributes & classification

Van Leeuwen, Jean. *Emma Bean.* Illustrated by Juan Wijngaard. Penguin USA, 1993. ISBN 0-8037-1393-2
Emma is a stuffed animal that watches Molly from birth to adolescence.
time, data gathering & analyzing

Viorst, Judith. *Alexander, Who Used to Be Rich Last Sunday.* Illustrated by Ray Cruz. Simon and Schuster, 1978. ISBN 0-689-30602-4
Alexander, Que ere rico el dominogo pasado. Simon and Schuster, 1989. ISBN 0-689-31590-2
Alexander and his two older brothers each get a dollar from their grandparents on Sunday. Alexander wants to save his money for a walkie-talkie, but he is the victim of temptation and accidents. Litle by little, his money goes until he is left with nothing but bus tokens. (See page 50.)
numeration, estimation, computation, money, problem solving, probability, time

Wells, Rosemary. *Waiting for the Evening Star.* Illustrated by Susan Jeffers. Penguin USA, 1993. ISBN 0-8037-1399-1
Time moves slowly on a farm in Vermont in the 1910s.
time, patterns

Wiesner, David. *Tuesday.* Houghton, 1991. ISBN 0-395-55113-7
Gleeful frogs flying on lily pads invade the village during the night, entering houses and startling dogs and a man enjoying a midnight snack. The next day, police and other investigators find no evidence, except lily pads all over the place. (See page 51.)
time, problem solving, data gathering & analyzing, patterns

Williams, Vera. *A Chair for My Mother.* Morrow, 1982. ISBN 0-688-00915-8
After a fire burns all their belongings, a family saves their change to buy a comfortable chair for the mother to rest in after her hard day's work as a waitress.
money, computation, problem solving

Wood, Audrey. *The Napping House.* Illustrated by Don Wood. Harcourt, 1991. ISBN 0-15-256708-9
Available in Big Book format.
This tale builds a pile of sleeping creatures and then puts a wakeful flea at the top. The humor, vocabu-

lary, and use of color make this book outstanding.
time, patterns, attributes & classification, measurement

Young, Ed. *Seven Blind Mice.* Putnam, 1992.
ISBN 0-399-22261-8
Each of seven blind mice sees one part of the elephant and, based on that limited information, identifies it incorrectly. The mice are ordered in two ways—by the days of the week and by ordinals.
perspective, data gathering & analyzing, attributes & classification, numeration, time

Zemach, Harve. *The Judge: An Untrue Tale.* Illustrated by Margot Zemach. Farrar, 1969.
ISBN 0-374-33960-0
In this rhyming book, one after another witness is brought before the judge. Each witness adds another detail to a description of a monster who is heading their way. The judge declares each testimony untrue and orders the witnesses to prison. After the last prisoner is dragged away, the monster enters and eats the judge.
data gathering & analyzing, attributes & classification, patterns

Zolotow, Charlotte. *Mister Rabbit and the Lovely Present.* Illustrated by Maurice Sendak. HarperCollins, 1962. ISBN 0-06-026946-4
A little girl needs an idea for a present for her mother. A rabbit helps her narrow down the choices. In so doing, we go through a series of articles and their attributes.
attributes & classification

APPENDICES

APPENDIX A: COUNTING BOOKS

Anno, Mitsumasa. *Anno's Counting Book.* HarperCollins, 1977. ISBN 0-690-01288-8
Against a barren landscape, Anno presents sets of numbers and their numerals, the months and seasons, and even builds us a village. There is so much to count and examine here that one look through is not enough.

Anno, Mitsumasa. *Anno's Counting House.* Putnam, 1982. ISBN 0-399-20896-8
Through cut-out windows and exterior and interior views, we watch ten children move from a house on one side of the street to a house on the other. As they move, we can count and see many combinations of ten.

Archambault, John. *Counting Sheep.* Illustrated by John Rombola. Henry Holt, 1989. ISBN 0-8050-1135-8
Available in Big Book and Small Book formats from SRA.
Tired of counting sheep in order to fall asleep, a boy counts many different animals.

Aylesworth, Jim. *One Crow: A Counting Rhyme.* HarperCollins, 1988. ISBN 0-397-32175-9
We count crows and watch the seasons change.

Bang, Molly. *Ten, Nine, Eight.* Morrow, 1983. ISBN 0-688-00907-7
We count backwards from ten with a little girl and her father as nighttime comes.

Brett, Jan. *The Twelve Days of Christmas.* Putnam, 1990. ISBN 0-399-22197-2
In this lush rendition of the counting Christmas carol, Brett uses the frames around each picture to tell a wordless love story.

Brisson, Pat. *Benny's Pennies.* Illustrated by Bob Barner. Doubleday, 1993. ISBN 0-385-41602-4
Benny starts out with five pennies and ends up with none. (See page 9.)

Carle, Eric. *Rooster's Off to See the World.* Picture Book Studios, 1991. ISBN 0-88708-042-1
The pattern of animals joining and leaving the procession is similar to that in many folktales.

Chandra, Deborah. *Miss Mabel's Table.* Illustrated by Max Grover. Harcourt, 1994. ISBN 0-15-276712-6
In a "This is the house that Jack built" manner, ingredients for pancakes are assembled on Miss Mabel's table in her restaurant. When she arrives, she makes the pancakes and serves them to the ten people she passed or met on the way to work.

Charlip, Remy. *Thirteen.* Simon and Schuster, 1984. ISBN 0-02-718120-0
On thirteen pages, we follow episodes in each of thirteen stories in this unusual, puzzling book.

Christelow, Eileen. *Five Little Monkeys.* Houghton, 1991. ISBN 0-395-54434-3
The familiar folk rhyme is the basis for this counting book.

Cleveland, David. *The April Rabbits.* Illustrated by Nurit Karlin. Scholastic, 1986. ISBN 0-590-42369-X
Each day of April, David discovers that number of rabbits in his life. This is a good counting book because the story is funny and it combines ordinal and cardinal numbers.

Crews, Donald. *Ten Black Dots.* Morrow, 1986. ISBN 0-688-060678-4
Simple black dots in all sorts of environments become our counting device.

Crowther, Robert. *The Most Amazing Hide & Seek Counting Book.* Penguin USA, 1981. ISBN 0-670-48997-2
First find the hidden animals, then count them.

Cunrea, Olivier. *Deep Down Underground.* Simon and Schuster, 1989. ISBN 0-02-732861-9
This counting book centers around a mole who, as it digs, sets off action and reaction among the underground creatures. Here the numbers and the creatures get equal billing.

Edwards, Richard. *Ten Tall Oak Trees.* Illustrated by Caroline Crossland. Morrow, 1993. ISBN 0-688-04621-5
We watch as a stand of oak trees is eliminated one by one.

Ehlert, Lois. *Fish Eyes: A Book You Can Count On.* Harcourt, 1992. ISBN 0-15-228051-0
With vivid colors and images of fish, we count from one to ten.

Echenberg, Fritz. *Dancing in the Moon: Counting Rhymes.* Harcourt, 1975. ISBN 0-15-623811-X
Numbers from one to twenty are presented in this book of animals dancing in the night.

Feelings, Muriel. *Moja Means One: A Swahili Counting Book.* Penguin USA, 1987. ISBN 0-8037-5777-7
The title explains the book, but the illustrations, in addition to providing the corresponding numerals for items, give us a great deal of information about African village life.

Fleming, Denise. *Count!* Henry Holt, 1992. ISBN 0-8050-1595-7 This counting book takes us through many parts of the animal kingdom. The beginning page tells us to count, and the last page says "Count Again!" and you want to do just that.

Freschet, Berniece. *The Ants Go Marching.* Simon and Schuster, 1973. ISBN 0-684-13250-8
The familiar folk song is depicted in this counting book.

Geisert, Arthur. *Pigs from One to Ten.* Houghton, 1992. ISBN 0-395-58519-8
Ten piglets find their "lost place with huge stone configurations," a tablet with Arabic numerals, after much trial and travail.

Gerstein, Mordicai. *Roll Over!* Random, 1988. ISBN 0-517-55209-4
This common folk counting rhyme is illustrated with detailed and amusing watercolors.

Giganti, Paul. *Each Orange Had 8 Slices: A Counting Book.* Illustrated by Donald Crews. Morrow, 1992. ISBN 0-688-10429-0
Children can count or multiply in this book of sets and numbers.

Giganti, Paul. *How Many Snails?* Illustrated by Donald Crews. Morrow, 1988. ISBN 0-688-06370-5
As we view different sites, we count a variety of items. Then we count subsets.

Hoban, Tana. *Count and See.* Simon and Schuster, 1972. ISBN 0-02-744800-2
Hoban gives us interesting objects to count in her black-and-white photographs.

Hoban, Tana. *Twenty-Six Letters and Ninety-Nine Cents.* Morrow, 1987. ISBN 0-688-06362-4
Photographs show us letters, which seem to be the plastic raised letters on magnets commonly used on refrigerators, and coins. The book is divided into two parts to show the letters and money separately. As a nice touch, an amount of money is shown in two or three combinations of coins.

Hort, Lenny. *How Many Stars in the Sky?* Illustrated by James Ransome. Morrow, 1991. ISBN 0-688-10104-6

A father and child attempt to count the stars.

Inkpen, Mick. *One Bear at Bedtime*. Little, 1988. ISBN 0-316-41889-7

We count all the items on each page, but eventually we search the pages for missing caterpillars.

Kitchen, Bert. *Animal Numbers*. Penguin USA, 1987. ISBN 0-8037-0459-3

Fifteen animals are shown with their offspring, and readers are asked to determine how many are in each brood.

Lindbergh, Reeve. *Midnight Farm*. Penguin USA, 1987. ISBN 0-8037-0333-3

As a mother and child take a late night farm tour, we get a subtle and beautiful counting book.

Loomis, Christine. *One Cow Coughs: A Counting Book for the Sick and Miserable*. Houghton, 1994. ISBN 0-395-67899-4

We count from one to ten farm animals who are ailing, and then from ten to one as each group feels better.

McMillan, Bruce. *Counting Wildflowers*. Morrow, 1986. ISBN 0-688-02860-8

These are beautiful photographs we can use to count the wildflower blossoms. We can also concentrate on numerous properties.

Micklethwait, Lucy. *I Spy Two Eyes: Numbers in Art.* Morrow, 1993. ISBN 0-688-12642-1

The paintings of the masters illustrate this counting book, and we search through well-known paintings to find the numbers sequentially.

O'Brien, Mary. *Counting Sheep to Sleep*. Illustrated by Bobette McCarthy. Little, 1992. ISBN 0-316-62206-0

A little girl on a farm makes sure all the animals are ready for bed before going to bed herself. The sheep, however, refuse to cooperate, and she ends up in a sheep roundup before they all go to sleep.

O'Keefe, Susan Heyboer. *One Hungry Monster: A Counting Book in Rhyme*. Illustrated by Lynn Munsinger. Little, 1989. ISBN 0-316-63385-2

Not only is this house infested with monsters, but they are rude, boisterous, and noisy monsters. Most importantly, however, they are hungry, and after they are assembled, one by one, the boy gets food for them, also one by one. This is a funny counting book with lots to enjoy.

Philpot, Lorna and Philpot, Graham. *Amazing Anthony Ant*. Random, 1994. ISBN 0-679-85622-6

Based on the song "The Ants Go Marching," this book combines lift-the-flap counting, alternative rhymes and phrases, and even throws in a maze.

Reiss, John J. *Numbers*. Simon and Schuster, 1982. ISBN 0-02-776150-9

Reiss takes us all the way to 1000 in this beautiful counting book of simple shapes and vibrant colors.

Ryan, Pam Muñoz. *One Hundred Is a Family*. Illustrated by Benrei Huang. Hyperion, 1994. ISBN 1-56282-672-7

This counting book emphasizes families of all kinds. We start with several small family units, build extended families, and end up with a world family working to make the earth better. The numbers go from one to ten and then by tens to one hundred.

Sis, Peter. *Going Up! A Color Counting Book*. Morrow, 1989. ISBN 0-688-08126-6

An elevator goes up through an apartment building, and on each floor Mary is joined by a neighbor. But such neighbors! There are many costumes and, of course, there are colors. We count neighbors, colors, and floors. There are cardinal numbers as well.

Sloat, Teri. *From One to One Hundred.* Dutton, 1991. ISBN 0-525-44764-4
In this book, we count sets. The pages are crowded and, at times, confusing, but the target sets are placed in isolation at the bottom of the page. We count from one to ten and, by tens, to one hundred.

Tafuri, Nancy. *Who's Counting?* Morrow, 1986. ISBN 0-688-06131-1
Tafuri's unusual perspectives illustrate this counting book.

Walsh, Ellen Stoll. *Mouse Count.* Illustrated by Diane D'Andrade. Harcourt, 1991. ISBN 0-15-256023-8
Ten mice fall asleep in the meadow as a big snake lurks nearby. He collects the mice, dropping them into a jar and counting them. One mouse tricks him into going out for more mice and, one by one, the mice leave in a countdown.

Wise, William. *Ten Sly Piranhas.* Illustrated by Victoria Chess. Penguin USA, 1993. ISBN 0-8037-1201-4
A school of piranhas is decimated one by one.

Wormell, Christopher. *A Number of Animals.* Creative Editions, 1993. ISBN 0-88682-625-X
We count numbers from one to ten as a chick searches for its mother.

Appendix B: Professional Resources

*Curriculum and Evaluation Standards for School
    Mathematics*
    National Council of Teachers of Mathematics
    1906 Association Dr.
    Reston, VA 22091
    (800) 235-7566

Let's Talk Math
    Pat Lilburn & Pam Rawson
    Heinemann, 1994
    ISBN 0-435-08348-1

*Linking Mathematics and Language: Practical
    Classroom Activities*
    Richard D. McCallum
    Pippin Publishing, 1994
    ISBN 0-88751-038-8

Mathematics Their Way
    Mary Baratta-Lorton
    Addison-Wesley, 1976
    ISBN 0-201-04320-3

Mathwise
    Arthur A. Hyde and Pamela R. Hyde
    Heinemann, 1991
    ISBN 0-435-08311-2

Quest 2000 Exploring Mathematics
    Textbook Series
    Addison-Wesley, 1995

Read Any Good Math Lately?
    David J. Whitin and Sandra Wilde
    Heinemann, 1992
    ISBN 0-435-08334-1

Skills and Concepts Guide
    Pam Schiller
    SRA, 1994
    ISBN 0-02-685989-0

Under Construction: Beginning Math
    Pam Schiller and Lynne Peterson
    SRA, 1994
    ISBN 0-02-685997-1

Under Construction: Foundations of Math
    Pam Schiller and Lynne Peterson
    SRA, 1994
    ISBN 0-02-686871-1

Boldfaced titles and page numbers indicate titles and activities in Section 1.

INDEX

Topics & Concepts